American Language Hub

LEVEL 5A
Workbook

with Key + access to Audio

macmillan education

Macmillan Education Limited
4 Crinan Street
London N1 9XW

Companies and representatives throughout the world

American Language Hub Level 5A Workbook with Key
ISBN 978-1-380-04759-5
American Language Hub Level 5A Workbook with Key + access to Audio
ISBN 978-1-380-04753-3

Written by Signature Manuscripts

Signature Manuscripts has asserted their right to be identified as the author of this work in accordance with the Copyright, Designs and Patents Act 1988.

First published 2020

Original design by emc design ltd
Page make-up by SPi Global
Cover design based on original design by Restless
Cover photograph by plainpicture/Cavan Images, Getty Images/Luís Henrique Boucault
Picture research by Emily Taylor

The authors and publishers would like to thank the following for permission to reproduce their photographs:

Alamy/Mackney p36(tl); **Getty Images**/10'000 Hours p25, Getty Images/AFP/Philippe Huguen p15, Getty Images/Ty Allison p33, Getty Images/Apexphotos p14, Getty Images/Arterra p30(tl), Getty Images/AscentXmedia p35, Getty Images/Thomas Barwick pp5, 12, Getty Images/Sydney Bourne p29(tr), Getty Images/Bill Brooks p18(tl), Getty Images/Claudia Burlotti p4(tr), Getty Images/Caiaimage/Trevor Adeline p6, Getty Images/Caiaimage/Agnieszka Olek p37, Getty Images/Caiaimage/Chris Ryan p32, Getty Images/Cavan Images p34, Getty Images/Tom Cockrem p23, Getty Images/Design Pics Inc p30(tr), Getty Images/EyeEm/Severin Matusek p36(br), Getty Images/Georgijevic p26, Getty Images/Glow Wellness p29(tl), Getty Images/Hero Images p13,Getty Images/iStockphoto p7,Getty Images/Roo Lewis p36(bl), Getty Images/Maremagnum p16, Getty Images/Nomad p4(br), Getty Images/Seb Oliver p20, Getty Images/Miguel Sanz p38, Getty Images/SolStock p21, Getty Images/David Aaron Troy p8, Getty Images/Universal Images Group p17, Getty Images/VCG p22, Getty Images/Westend61 pp10, 19, 27, Getty Images/Tadao Yamamoto p18(tr), Getty Images/Zoonar RF p11

Additional sources: Ryan, R. M. & Deci, E. L. (2000), *Self-determination theory and the facilitation of intrinsic motivation, social development, and well-being*, American Psychologist, (pp68–78), https://dx.doi.org/10.1037/0003-066X.55.1.68, p36; Deci, E. L., & Ryan, R. M. (2012), *Motivation, personality, and development within embedded social contexts: An overview of self-determination theory*, in R. M. Ryan (Ed.), The Oxford Handbook of Human Motivation (pp85–107), Oxford, UK: Oxford University Press, p36; Ryan, R. M. & Deci, E. L. (2017), Self-Determination Theory: Basic Psychological Needs in Motivation, Development, and Wellness, New York: Guilford Publishing, p36

Printed and bound in Uruguay

2022
2

Contents

VOCABULARY
Clothes and fashion; Metaphors

A Choose the correct options to complete the sentences.

1 For most of us, it's in our nature to *follow* / *fit* a trend because being different is so much harder.

2 There's no need to wear a suit when meeting the team leader – *casual* / *scruffy* clothes will be fine.

3 I wonder where I can find a dressy *uniform* / *outfit* for Jen's wedding.

4 All it takes is for one influential person to wear something bold and he or she can *set* / *stand* a new trend.

5 Recently, people have become much more conscious of the type of *costumes* / *sportswear* they work out in at the gym.

6 One advantage of a school *uniform* / *costume* is that students who don't have fashionable or designer clothes don't feel left out.

7 Jed wants to be different – he always chooses his clothes so that he *stands* / *sets* out from the crowd.

8 I can't play tennis after work – I forgot to put my sports *code* / *gear* in the car.

9 George is a big guy, and he prefers to buy *scruffy* / *oversized* clothes from a special outlet.

10 I think I need a size smaller – this shirt looks kind of *baggy* / *scruffy* on me.

B Match the phrases in bold (1–10) in the article with the metaphors, which have the same meaning, in the box below.

are on a tight budget catches your eye for peanuts in the long run make a seamless transition off-the-rack snapped up tailor-made throwing money down the drain wind you up

1 ______
2 ______
3 ______
4 ______
5 ______
6 ______
7 ______
8 ______
9 ______
10 ______

The cool style guru

Have you ever wanted to upgrade your look, but felt confused by the range of options available? Does the need to buy dress clothes for work [1]**make you stressed**?

Do you go clothes shopping only to find the best things have already been [2]**bought**? Can't find anything that [3]**appeals to you**? Are you tired of [4]**wasting money** on clothes that just aren't right for you? With us, you can [5]**change effortlessly** from looking, well, let's say not your best – to looking like a million dollars!

We'll match top-quality clothes that'll look good on you immediately but, [6]**eventually**, you'll see just what a difference being well-dressed will make to your prospects.

We have a range of services – from [7]**made in a factory** to [8]**made just for you** – so, even if you [9]**can't spend a lot of money**, we promise to make you look good. We're confident that when you see the results, your life will be transformed, and you will have a wardrobe to be proud of – [10]**for very little money**.

Check out our website for more information!

GRAMMAR
Nominal clauses

A Match numbers (1–6) to letters (a–f) to form full sentences.

1 It should not need pointing out ____
2 The fact that he dresses nicely ____
3 How can something as simple as having an ironed shirt ____
4 For many people, dressing nicely means ____
5 As far as I'm concerned, to look good ____
6 The clothes you wear should not ____

a make a positive impression on others?
b reflects the seriousness with which he treats his position.
c that you have a duty to protect the company's reputation.
d influence others' opinion of you, but they do.
e is to feel good.
f little more than making sure their clothes are new or clean.

B Write one word in each blank to complete the sentences.

1 I think you'll like this jacket, and ____ may surprise you to learn that it costs less than $40.
2 We are left with the problem of ____ to address the complaints about our products.
3 The fact ____ you are employed on a full-time contract gives you certain privileges.
4 I regret ____ finding out more about the company before I went for an interview there.
5 The reason I objected to the sales clerk ____ that he had a bad attitude.
6 We may never know the reason ____ she did what she did.
7 They will be going on vacation in July, but ____ they're going is still undecided.
8 ____ you do in your own time is your own affair.

C Complete the second sentence so that it has a similar meaning to the first sentence using the words in bold. Write between two and five words, including the word given.

1 Dissatisfaction with clothing and appearance can be a problem for many these days.
OF
Many people face ____ dissatisfaction with clothing and appearance.

2 That uniforms are still widely worn in schools is common knowledge.
FACT
____ uniforms are still widely worn in schools is common knowledge.

3 It's not important what she spends her money on.
HOW
____ is not important.

4 To wear second-hand clothes is not a problem for me.
MIND
I ____ second-hand clothes.

PRONUNCIATION
Linking /r/

A Read the sentences aloud, paying attention to the way you pronounce the underlined sections.

1 My <u>car is</u> a lot less expensive than I thought it would be.
2 I <u>wore a</u> suit and felt very stylish.
3 <u>We're already</u> walking to the store.
4 Get one today! <u>They're only</u> $5!
5 I didn't plan to buy anything, but I saw a great shirt <u>for a</u> friend.
6 The things in that boutique <u>are expensive</u>.
7 And <u>you're almost</u> certain you saw that man stealing?
8 I found a <u>hair in</u> my food!

1.1 **B Listen to the sentences from Exercise A. Practice saying the sentences in the same way as the speakers do in the recording.**

GRAMMAR
Comparatives and superlatives

A Choose the correct options to complete the comments about a blog post.

iamthemusicman
2 days ago

I agree with what you say about popular music and originality. But we need to remember that musicians and producers need to attract the listener's attention [1]***as quickly as / quicker than*** possible. Sometimes, this involves producing unusual, trendsetting music, but since listeners don't always react well to [2]***dramatically / marginally*** different styles – at least not at first – it is sometimes safer to work within the boundaries of the [3]***later / latest*** trends.

Like | Comment | Share

fitbit46
5 days ago

I like what you said about music and working out. I'm a fitness instructor and for such activities, I tend to think volume is a factor – my rule is the [4]***louder than / louder*** the volume, the faster the workout. I also think we need music with [5]***a higher / the highest*** rate of beats per minute (bpm) than our heartbeat to help energize us for physical work. However, I don't think increased bpm or volume helps with creative work. [6]***Easily the most / By far the*** creative work is done, in my opinion, when the music is neither too loud nor too quiet, nor too fast nor too slow.

Like | Comment | Share

jazz4life
2 weeks ago

I think our musical tastes can be a good indicator of our personalities. When I was younger, I listened to [7]***the far highest / a considerably higher*** number of hard rock, indie and metal bands. I associate that with a time when I was more introverted but maybe also a lot more creative. Now, I listen to a [8]***great / far*** deal more jazz and soul. I'm a little less creative than I was, but I am a lot more outgoing, sociable and confident. That said, this is probably very subjective. I don't want to make any generalizations as [9]***more deeply / deeper*** analysis is needed to prove any link.

Like | Comment | Share

B Match the beginnings of the sentences (1–8) to the endings (a–h).

1 You're just the best ___
2 I think we have a great deal ___
3 Break for lunch, did you say? That is far ___
4 For some people, having trendy clothes is every bit ___
5 Even if I worked twice ___
6 We agreed that pronunciation is easily ___
7 A greater than ___
8 The upgrade to business class more than ___

a as many hours, I don't think I would get the job done in time.
b and away the best idea I've heard all day.
c and I don't know what I'd do without you.
d more to learn about how our choices are manipulated by marketing people.
e the most difficult aspect of learning English.
f as important as practicality – if not more so.
g made up for the delay to my flight.
h expected number of people attended the event.

VOCABULARY
Experimenting with prefixes and suffixes

A Choose the correct options to complete the sentences.

1 Their online vlog became ***popularish / hyper-influential*** when they got millions of subscribers.

2 Harry's not very ***tech-savvy / tech-friendly***. In fact, he can barely use a word processor.

3 Is your watch ***water-prone / waterproof***? If not, I'd take it off before you go in.

4 That video I made was very ***amateury / amateurish***, but it was my first one and I've learned a lot of tricks of the trade since then.

5 Ann is so ***disaster-prone / hyper-disaster***! She broke her phone, TV and tablet all in the same week!

6 Be careful because, once you delete something, you can't ***redelete / undelete*** it and get it back.

7 I like what the program does, but I don't find it very ***user-friendly / user-savvy*** – it took me a long time just to learn the basics.

8 Look – you were ***ultra-influential / super-lucky*** to get this job, so try to make the best of it.

B Rewrite the words in bold by adding a prefix or a suffix. Make any other necessary changes. More than one answer is sometimes possible.

1 These **heat** gloves are perfect for handling hot pans in the kitchen.

______

2 I'm hoping to raise a **large** amount of money to get this business up and running.

______

3 Sara's sick of reading **spam** comments about online articles.

______

4 He was going to buy a house, but he was forced to **think** when he lost his job.

______

5 I thought his jokes were really **cheese**.

______

6 The politician got into trouble because she said something without realizing her microphone had been **muted**.

______

7 Don't worry; this tablet is **idiot**. There's no way you can do any harm by pressing the wrong button.

______

8 They would never take a risk on this investment – you know that they're always **cautious** in their business decisions.

______

PRONUNCIATION
Emphatic stress

1.2 **A** Listen to these pairs of sentences. Underline one word in each sentence that has emphatic stress.

1 He's suggesting one solution, but there are others.
He's suggesting one solution, is that the best he can do?

2 They told me to work on this project, so that's what I'm doing.
They said the same to me, and that's what I am doing.

3 He suggested that the biggest problem is overseas sales.
But you don't realize that the biggest problem is overseas sales.

4 I can do it; the question is whether I want to do it.
I can do it, too, but I don't know when.

5 Do you think this will be a problem?
Without question, this will be a problem.

B Practice saying the sentences in the same way as the speakers do in the recording in Exercise A.

C Decide where to add emphatic stress in these sentences.

1 I was determined not to say anything that could get me in trouble.

2 Contrary to what you said, I do enjoy gardening.

3 Bill got the contract and a promotion, so he's happy.

1.3 **D** Listen to check your answers to Exercise C.

READING

A PREDICT You are going to read an article about selfies. Before you read, answer the questions.

1 Do you post selfies? If so, how often and how many?

2 What do you think motivates people who frequently post selfies?

B READ FOR MAIN IDEA Read *The new narcissism?* and match the paragraphs (1–5) to the summaries of each paragraph (a–e).

Paragraph 1 ____
Paragraph 2 ____
Paragraph 3 ____
Paragraph 4 ____
Paragraph 5 ____

a People who take and post a lot of selfies want to be perceived in a particular way.

b It is not yet clear if selfies are creating cultural change, for example, making people more open or less concerned about privacy.

c While selfies may have a longer history, the availability of technology and equipment is what made them a wider phenomenon in recent years.

d Despite criticism, selfies have been exhibited as a form of art and used to promote it, so it may be premature to say they have a negative impact.

e The first noted use of the word was in the early 2000s. Since then, its usage has steadily increased.

C WORK OUT MEANING Read the article again, paying particular attention to the underlined words (1–6). Find words in the article which have a contrasting meaning.

1 abating ____________
2 hostility ____________
3 ubiquitous ____________
4 plausible ____________
5 mundane ____________, ____________
6 reserved ____________, ____________

D WORK OUT MEANING Now match the words (1–6) to their definitions (a–f).

a seen/done/found everywhere ____
b quiet, not easily showing emotions ____
c believable ____
d becoming less ____
e boring or ordinary ____
f showing opposition or dislike ____

E REFLECT Have you changed your opinion of selfies after reading the article? Why/Why not?

The new NARCISSISM?

Of all the trends created by the digital revolution, one that often divides people is the fad of taking 'selfies'. Some find it baffling, others say it is harmless fun. But we can all agree that after two decades, it seems to be increasing every year rather than [1]<u>abating</u>. So, what do we know about this phenomenon?

1 Where did it come from?

The word 'selfie', it is alleged, originated in Australia. While for the die-hard selfie-haters out there the act of snapping and posting photos might increase feelings of [2]<u>hostility</u>, the use of '-*ie*' or '-*y*' is actually a friendly diminutive. Words like 'barbie' for barbeque or 'Mikey' for 'Michael' are endearing terms and a common feature of spoken English in Australia. The first recorded use of the word is said to be from a young Australian man in a public forum in 2002. In 2013, 'selfie' became the Oxford English Dictionary's word of the year. It is now used in everyday language.

2 Origins and development

Photographs that appear to be taken on devices similar to selfie sticks date back as far as 1926. But selfies really took off with the arrival of the front-facing camera in 2003. Before that, of course, people had been taking pictures of themselves with their cell phones: but selfies as we know them were comparatively rare, whereas now they are [3]<u>ubiquitous</u>. Type in 'selfie' on Instagram and you get close to 300 million results!

3 Look at me!

Is vanity or narcissism really driving this phenomenon? Some would say selfies are not about self-promotion, but simply a way of sharing new experiences with friends and family. The fact that many people post pictures of themselves doing exciting or unusual things makes this explanation seem [4]<u>plausible</u>. But when you consider that people also take pictures of themselves doing [5]<u>mundane</u> things like having breakfast, it seems unlikely it is the whole story. One theory is that it is a way for people to reimagine themselves, to present a different image to the world and to experiment with different identities. It's a way of saying, 'This is how I want to be seen'.

4 Cultural change

The selfie explosion does seem to have had a cultural and social influence. The British, for example, are allegedly perceived of as being [6]reserved, if not actually shy – they are definitely less often described as open or outgoing. Yet the selfie trend has taken hold in the UK as much as anywhere. No doubt, the digital age has encouraged people, especially the young, to make more personal information generally available. I wonder if the era of selfies presents a genuine cultural and social shift, or will there be a reaction against it?

5 Can selfies be art?

This might seem like a silly question. But I have heard one commentator say it is a new 'folk art' that is adding significantly to the language of photography. Exhibits at established galleries have displayed selfies. Whether you agree with this or not, Museum Selfie Day, a trend started by project coordinator Mar Dixon, definitely brings selfie-takers closer to art. In museums and galleries, the public are encouraged to take selfies of themselves in front of famous pieces. In the future, selfies might prove useful to cultural historians interested in the goings-on of people in the early 21st century. Perhaps it's too soon to label this trend as simply a good or a bad thing.

Glossary

alleged (adj) claimed to be true

baffling (adj) confusing, difficult to understand

vanity (n) being too interested in your own appearance

LISTENING

A Imagine that you and your friends are going to make a short video of the previous year's trends, most popular videos, vlogs, etc. What would you include? Give reasons for your answers.

B 1.4 **LISTEN FOR RECOMMENDATIONS** Listen to a conversation between two friends about making a video review of the year. Check (✓) the items which the speakers are going to include.

1. celebrity endorsements ☐
2. viral videos ☐
3. important news stories ☐
4. an image of a TV presenter ☐
5. newspaper headlines ☐
6. cartoons ☐
7. memes ☐
8. home videos of friends ☐
9. clips of influencers/trendsetters ☐

C 1.4 **LISTEN FOR DETAIL** Listen again and complete the sentences with one or two words in each blank.

1. The GenZ video is a ________ of the past year's events.
2. Viewers did not give this year's video positive ________.
3. In one recent viral video, a ________ has an accident.
4. ________ and coloring can be used with pictures of famous people.
5. The woman suggests including short pieces of ________ from movies or cartoons.
6. They decide to include memes which were popular with their ________.
7. As a ________, Daisy Trekker is an influencer, personality and trendsetter.
8. They think it's important to include vlogs that are ________ to draw traffic to their own video.

Glossary

pace (n) speed

viral (adj) very popular and spreading very quickly, especially on the internet

D **REFLECT** Are internet trendsetters more influential than traditional role models such as movies, music, TV stars or athletes? Why/Why not?

WRITING

A You are going to read a blog post. Before you read, think about these questions.

1 How does a blog post differ from other kinds of writing?
2 What features do you think would make a blog post more attractive to readers?
3 What can you do to improve the ranking of a blog or website?

B Read *4 tips for a successful blog post* and match the headings (a–d) to the paragraphs (1–4).

a Structure your posts
b Grow your blog
c Think before you write
d Know your audience, know yourself

C **MAKING YOUR BLOG POST SUCCESSFUL** Read the blog post again and answer the questions.

1 What are the keywords (the most frequently repeated words) in the tips?
2 How will organizing your blog post in the way advised improve search engine-friendliness?
3 What else can be done to attract more readers?
4 What 'call to action' does the writer use at the end of the post?

WRITING PRACTICE

A **PREPARE** You are going to write a blog post about a current trend. Choose from this list, or use your own idea. Write notes about your chosen topic.

- fashion (clothes)
- a personal item
- a new gadget
- recreational activity
- superhero movies

B **PLAN** Organize your notes from Exercise A into a plan.

- Use an appropriate structure for a blog post (including paragraph headings).
- Think about who your target audience is.
- Choose a keyword or phrase for repetition.

C **WRITE** Write your article in 200–300 words. Use your plan to help you.

4 TIPS FOR A SUCCESSFUL BLOG POST

A successful blog post needs to be both search engine-friendly and reader-friendly. The two go together, and by following these tips, you will enhance your online profile and produce more successful blog posts.

1 ___

What exactly is the purpose of your blog? What is your message? And what action do you want people to take when they've finished reading? Think about these points and write some notes.

2 ___

Successful blog posts have a clear target audience and their message is tailored accordingly. This means thinking about what will attract your readers' attention but also drawing in the curious browser. This also means working out what *your* selling point is. Is it your expertise, your passion for the subject, your taste, style or personal viewpoint? Build on your strengths.

3 ___

Successful blog posts are well-organized. Obvious, I know, but many posts read as if the writer just wrote the first thing that came into their head. Every post should have:

- an introduction
- a main body
- a conclusion.

Write notes about what you want to put in each section. This is a summary of your post – now you can start to fill it in. It is a feature of successful blog posts that they give each paragraph an informative and eye-catching heading using keywords. This is important because the search engine will pick up the main topics and help to improve your ranking.

4 ___

To increase both your readership and your position on the search engine, add links to previous posts on the same topic, and keep adding posts to your website so your audience and the search engine know you're still there.

For more tips on writing a successful blog post, click on the icon below.

Click here

VOCABULARY
Describing art

A Match the adjectives (1–8) to the definitions (a–h).

1 tedious ____
2 appalling ____
3 hilarious ____
4 thought-provoking ____
5 groundbreaking ____
6 unconventional ____
7 overrated ____
8 pretentious ____

a different from what people think is usual
b dreadful, awful
c extremely funny
d new and pioneering, innovative
e not as good as people say
f attempts to impress with qualities it doesn't have
g very boring
h makes you think

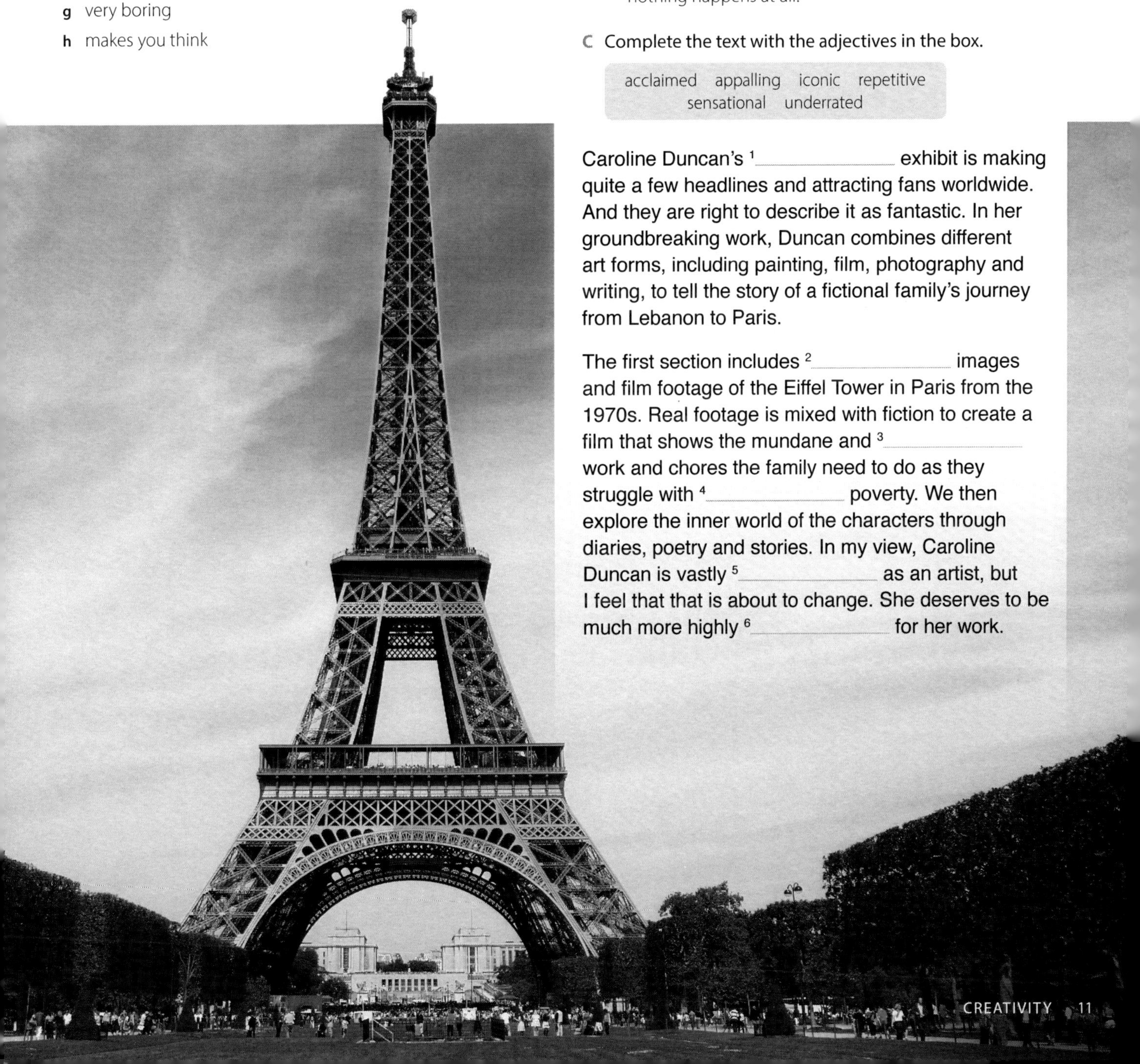

B Choose the correct words to complete the sentences.

1 An artist doesn't necessarily have to be ***groundbreaking / appalling*** to make good art.
2 Many hyped blockbusters are actually ***imaginative / overrated*** and disappointing.
3 Personally I found the movie ***pretentious / sensational*** – it felt like the director was just trying to show off how clever she is.
4 We think the play was supposed to be serious, but the acting was so bad it was actually ***iconic / hilarious***.
5 The painter's style is very ***tedious / unconventional*** – there is nobody that paints in the same way.
6 The painting is truly ***pretentious / thought-provoking*** – it makes you think about how we live in the modern world.
7 What a ***sensational / overrated*** performance by the lead actor – one of the best I've ever seen.
8 It was so ***groundbreaking / tedious*** – 90 minutes and nothing happens at all!

C Complete the text with the adjectives in the box.

acclaimed appalling iconic repetitive sensational underrated

Caroline Duncan's [1] ____ exhibit is making quite a few headlines and attracting fans worldwide. And they are right to describe it as fantastic. In her groundbreaking work, Duncan combines different art forms, including painting, film, photography and writing, to tell the story of a fictional family's journey from Lebanon to Paris.

The first section includes [2] ____ images and film footage of the Eiffel Tower in Paris from the 1970s. Real footage is mixed with fiction to create a film that shows the mundane and [3] ____ work and chores the family need to do as they struggle with [4] ____ poverty. We then explore the inner world of the characters through diaries, poetry and stories. In my view, Caroline Duncan is vastly [5] ____ as an artist, but I feel that that is about to change. She deserves to be much more highly [6] ____ for her work.

PRONUNCIATION
Contrastive stress

A Read the sentences aloud, paying attention to the contrastive stress on the underlined words.

1. Actually, I like a lot of modern art – it's abstract art I have difficulty with.
2. Why don't we go to the theater for a change, since we always go to the movies?
3. Although everyone says the new play is great, I found it very tedious.
4. I don't like opera, but I'm very interested in ballet.
5. While your eyes are drawn to the middle, what happens at the front is more exciting.
6. The movie was more of a romance than a thriller.
7. I much prefer landscape paintings – I'm not a fan of portraits.
8. No, I prefer listening to recorded music, not live music.

2.1 **B** Listen to the sentences from Exercise A. Practice saying the sentences in the same way as the speakers do in the recording.

GRAMMAR
Narrative tenses

A Choose the correct options to complete the sentences.

1. The exhibit space *was being prepared* / *was preparing* for the big opening when we arrived.
2. I jumped up the moment they *were calling* / *called* my name.
3. Everyone *was waiting* / *had waited* in suspense for the result to be announced.
4. We didn't stay at our usual hotel because it *was being damaged* / *had been damaged* in a fire the week before.
5. I was tired when I got home because I *have had* / *had had* to stay very late at work.
6. We *were telling* / *were told* the results would come out the following week.
7. Why *wasn't I informed* / *didn't I inform* about the change of plan?
8. The road was dangerous because it *had been snowing* / *has been snowing* during the night.

B Find and correct eight mistakes in the text. Sometimes more than one correct answer is possible.

Thursday May 23, 2019

THE MEETING

So – big day today. Important meeting with some clients so I had to get to the office early. I got up at five, had a quick cup of coffee and had left the house at 5:20. I got half way to the office when I realized that I had been forgetting my phone. Can you believe it? I drove for at least half an hour already, so I really didn't feel like going back, but I was having no choice. So, that delayed me by about an hour.

And when I finally got to the office, I gave a message that my boss wanted to see me urgently. I ran to her office. I could see through the glass door she talked to my clients, who already arrived. Oh no!

Luckily, she wasn't annoyed and my clients were fine. The meeting went well, and by lunchtime, we have agreed on everything.

VOCABULARY
Ideas and inspiration; Compound adjectives

A Complete the magazine interview with one word in each blank. The first letter is given to help you.

Do you find it hard to get started on a new project?

It takes time, yes. Of course, having the idea to begin with is the important part. If I know what I want to paint or sculpt, I'm eager to get started. But sometimes, I hit a [1]**w**__________ – I just have no ideas at all. When I'm – quite literally – working from a blank [2]**c**__________ right at the start of a project, I get a bit stressed.

What do you do when you're not inspired? How do you jump [3]s__________ your creativity?

I usually [4]**d**__________ inspiration from other artists. I go to galleries, look at pictures online, that sort of thing. I get a [5]**f**__________ perspective on things in that way. Sometimes I [6]**b**__________ ideas off friends and then I [7]**r**__________ with an idea. For me, it's important to communicate with other people, but then, to get into the right [8]**s**__________ of mind, I need to be alone. I [9]**t**__________ my instincts and it's never long before I'm working again.

Can you describe what happens when you get started?

That's when you won't see me for days – possibly weeks! I totally [10]**i**__________ myself in my work. During that time, nothing else matters. I would forget to eat if people didn't bring me food!

B Choose the correct options to complete the sentences.

1 Jim works long hours in the studio so he often listens to ***part / late***-night radio programs.
2 Ken got a ***part / self***-time job while studying for his doctorate.
3 In the acting world, you need to be ***thick / self***-skinned because you can get more criticism than praise sometimes.
4 I wouldn't like to be ***part / self***-employed. I'm happy working for my boss.
5 Flora left school and found a ***world / highly*** paid job with a TV production company.
6 Let's face it – the chances of anyone becoming a ***well / world***-famous singer are pretty slim.
7 I try to remain ***open / late***-minded about my job. If they offered me a transfer to a different branch, I like to think I would consider it.
8 If you work for yourself, you need to be a ***well / open***-motivated worker because it's tempting to take it easy.

PRONUNCIATION
Questions for comment or criticism

A Read the conversation aloud, paying attention to the intonation at the end of the questions.

Woman: Jake from our creative writing course says that he gets all his ideas in his dreams!
Man: Is he crazy? Dreams are so random. And I wouldn't be able to remember mine anyway.
Woman: He keeps a dream diary by his bed. That's a good idea, don't you think?
Man: How can you keep a diary of dreams? Dreams don't make any sense.
Woman: Aren't you being a bit negative? The diary might work for him and help with his stories.
Man: Who writes about dreaming? You need to write about something you actually know or have experienced. Isn't that the point?
Woman: Are you serious? Writing isn't just about what we know. Anyway I've started a diary myself. I set an alarm for the middle of the night. So, I can wake up in the middle of the dream.
Man: Why would you do that? You'll just be tired and feel even less creative the next day. Better to sleep well and then actually come up with some interesting ideas yourself.
Woman: Isn't that a bit dismissive? And why don't you read some of his stories before you decide it's a bad idea?

2.2 **B** Listen to the conversation from Exercise A. Then practice reading it in the same way as the speakers do in the recording.

GRAMMAR

Future in the past

A Match the beginnings of the sentences (1–6) to the endings (a–f).

1 We were going ___
2 Meeting Stella would ___
3 They were to ___
4 I was just ___
5 We weren't ___
6 Jenny and Fiona ___

a supposed to use the computer for personal use, but nobody said anything.
b about to go out when I got a phone call.
c were going on vacation the next day so they were packing.
d to call you, but we thought you might be sleeping.
e turn out to be an unforgettable experience.
f call us if there was any kind of problem.

B Choose the correct options (a, b or c) to complete the sentences.

1 The bridge ___ been completed last year but there were unexpected delays.
  a was to have
  b was
  c had to have

2 You ___ finish the reports before four o'clock. What happened?
  a were about to
  b would
  c were supposed to

3 Sorry – I interrupted you. You ___ something?
  a were about to say
  b would have said
  c weren't supposed to say

4 We were ___ go on vacation when we heard the news.
  a about just to
  b just about to
  c about to just

5 Who thought it ___ a good idea to play a trick on me?
  a would be
  b will be
  c had been

6 We knew he ___ a famous singer.
  a was always being
  b was always going to be
  c had always supposed to be

7 You had your instructions – you ___ me the minute you arrived.
  a were calling
  b were about to call
  c were to call

8 I didn't have much time with John because he ___ for Brazil the next day.
  a had been leaving
  b was leaving
  c would have left

READING

A PREDICT Look at the title of the article and the picture. Which words from the word cloud below do you think will appear in the article?

map **pilot** **engineer** bridge
creativity proposal **perspective** railway
carriage flag **survey** **overground**
construction **canvas**

B READ FOR GIST Read *The channel tunnel* quickly. Why did it take so long to create this transportation link between Britain and France?

C READ FOR DETAIL Read again and answer the questions.

1 Who put forward the first plan for a transportation link between the two countries?

2 Which proposal after 1979 did not involve an underwater tunnel?

3 How long did it take to build the tunnel?

D INFER MEANING Read the article again and choose the correct answer (a or b).

1 What do you understand by the use of the phrase 'finally agreed'? (Paragraph 1)

a The writer is unhappy about the tunnel.

b It had taken a long time to reach an agreement.

2 Why did engineers 'study the blueprints' despite problems between the two countries? (Paragraph 2)

a They had made a secret agreement with the authorities.

b They still believed that the project would be completed one day.

3 What can we infer from the sentence 'One British and one French worker were chosen by lottery to be the first to greet each other …'?

a France and Britain wanted to be seen as equals in the project.

b The workers wanted to congratulate each other.

E REFLECT Think about the answers to these questions.

1 Do you believe that this project was worth the time and money spent on it? Why/Why not?

2 What other impressive engineering projects, ancient or modern, can you name?

THE CHANNEL TUNNEL

It was in 1985 that British and French governments finally agreed to construct a tunnel under the English Channel. It would be one of the largest engineering projects undertaken by the UK. But the talks had begun a long time before that – since at least 1957 when Louis Armand's study group came up with a proposal for two railway tunnels, with a third smaller tunnel for maintenance running between them.

But dreams of a link between England and France go back even further than that. The first proposal was made by a French mining engineer, Albert Mathieu, at the beginning of the 19th century, who suggested a road tunnel that allowed horse-drawn carriages to pass between the two countries. When hostilities broke out between the English and the French, the plan was abandoned. Engineers continued to study the blueprints, however, and thought they could adapt their recently acquired expertise in building overground tunnels to building one under water.

By 1871, England and France were on friendly terms again and further surveys were completed, and this time, they got as far as deciding where to start tunneling. However, this plan, too, had to be abandoned following a change of government in England.

On several occasions over the next 100 years, the project looked as if it might be revived. But it wasn't until the 1970s that another serious attempt was made, when both sides agreed to start digging. However, this was stopped for economic reasons. A change in government in 1979 brought the project back to life. Although this time, there would be no public funding, so it had to be privately financed. The Channel Tunnel Company won the contract, with the same 1960 three-tunnels-in-one idea. Other proposals included: Eurobridge (a suspension bridge) and Euroute (a sea tunnel joining man-made islands).

Construction began in 1988 at Folkestone in England and Coquelles in France simultaneously, the idea being to meet in the middle. It turned into a race to see who could get there first. Tunnel-drilling machines, weighing 1000 tons and needing about 20 people to operate, were used to drill through the rock and chalk layers. After two years, the tunnels met in the middle. One British and one French worker were chosen by lottery to be the first to greet each other when the breakthrough was made.

This tremendous engineering project was finally completed by May 1994. It is now considered to be one of the seven wonders of the modern world.

Glossary

blueprint (n) a drawing or plan showing how to build a machine/building, etc

drill (v) to make a hole using a special machine/tool

ventilation (n) a system allowing fresh air to move around a building

LISTENING

A PREDICT Put the words in the correct columns. Which of these words would you use to describe the building in the picture?

appalling awesome groundbreaking iconic pretentious sensational thought-provoking unconventional

Positive	Negative	Neither positive nor negative
______	______	______
______	______	
______		
______		
______		

B ANTICIPATE CONTENT You are going to listen to part of a radio program called *Frank Gehry: life and work*. Look again at the picture in Exercise A. Answer the questions.

1 What is Frank Gehry's profession?

2 How successful is he?

3 Is his style traditional or unconventional?

4 Think of another question you expect to be answered in the program.

2.3 **C LISTEN FOR GIST** Listen to the program and check your predictions in Exercise B.

2.3 **D LISTEN FOR DETAIL** Listen again and complete the sentences with one or two words in each blank. Sometimes more than one answer is possible.

1 These days, architects like famous artists get admiration and ______.

2 While Gehry takes satisfaction in his achievements, he is not fond of ______.

3 Before achieving fame, Gehry had to deal with ______.

4 Gehry felt strongly that his buildings should mirror their ______.

5 Gehry is able to create striking and distinctive shapes through building with ______.

6 People who visit the Guggenheim Museum have been known to say that the building is ______ than the things in it.

Glossary

be a household name (phr) be very well-known

commission (n) a request for an artist to create a piece of work (for payment)

discipline (n) a subject that people study

signature style (n) style which is associated with a particular person

E REFLECT Think about the answers to these questions.

1 What style of architecture do you like (for example, modern or traditional)? Why?

2 Think about a famous building in your country. How would you describe it? Use the adjectives in Exercise A.

WRITING

A Which of these places would you most enjoy visiting and why?

- a gallery with works by unknown, living artists
- an exhibit of a well-known painter
- a museum with interesting objects from the past

B Read *Monet at the National Gallery* and match the paragraphs (1–5) to the brief paragraph summaries (a–e).

a the writer's opinion of the exhibit ____
b introducing the exhibit and its theme ____
c a more detailed look at the paintings ____
d how the exhibit is arranged ____
e revisiting the theme of the exhibit ____

Monet at the National Gallery

1 When you mention the name 'Monet', most people think 'water lilies', but this exhibit is entitled 'Monet and Architecture', which is not a connection most art lovers would make. French Impressionist painter Monet painted Rouen Cathedral several times and there are buildings in many of his paintings, but … architecture as an important theme?

2 Organized in such a way as to surprise and delight the visitor, the paintings are presented in an unusual fashion. You don't go from room to room looking at his early, middle and late periods; the idea is more than that you see how his later work was influenced by his early work. Monet, born in 1840, continued painting until the mid-1920s, so there is much to explore.

3 Examples of the Rouen Cathedral paintings are here, somehow making the weighty and massive construction seem ready to float away. This is also true of the Venice paintings. Already part of a floating city, the buildings of Venice seem to sail like gondolas on the water. There are paintings done in London, too, a city about which Monet boldly said, 'would be quite ugly if not for the fog'.

4 Buildings, though, are often just a focus point for other elements of the work, a point from which the eye is drawn into the painting. They are just another part of nature, subject to the same laws and conditions. You will come away with a sense of extraordinary beauty and the passing of time.

5 This is a wonderful exhibit that I would recommend to everyone – art lover or not. If you only know Monet for his water lilies, you don't know half the story.

C WRITING CONCISELY Find sentences or clauses in the review which express these ideas in a more concise way. Match each one to a grammatical feature.

1 The paintings are organized in such a way as to surprise and delight the visitor and are presented in an unusual fashion. ____
2 Monet, who was born in 1840, continued painting until the mid-1920s … ____
3 Monet was a French Impressionist painter who painted Rouen Cathedral several times … ____

a noun phrase
b reduced adjective clause
c participle clause

WRITING PRACTICE

A PREPARE You are going to write a review of a cultural or artistic event. Think about the answers to these questions and write notes.

1 Have you been to a cultural or artistic event recently (art/photography exhibit, museum, concert, book reading, etc)?
2 Where was it? What was on display or what happened? If it was an exhibit, who was the main artist? Was there a theme?
3 How was the event organized? How were the artworks / museum objects / different aspects presented?
4 What did you like or dislike about the event?

B PLAN Organize your notes from Exercise A into a plan.

- Use an appropriate structure for a review.
- Don't forget to give your recommendation in the last paragraph.

C WRITE Write your review in 220–260 words. Use your plan to help you.

VOCABULARY

Sustainability; Forming verbs from adjectives

A Choose the correct options to complete the article.

AIR POLLUTION

When it comes to air pollution, by far the worst [1]***depletions / emissions*** are those created by power stations which we use for electricity production. Some people seem to think that their activities are [2]***biodegradable / carbon-neutral*** just because they plant a few trees to [3]***consume / offset*** the damage caused by flying all over the world, but airplanes are not the cause of the worst damage.

We tend to think of electricity as clean and harmless because that is the form in which it seems to arrive in our homes – after all, we don't see the smoke pouring out of power stations because they are usually far from where we live. We sometimes conveniently 'forget' that fossil fuels aren't [4]***degradable / sustainable*** forms of energy, so we rarely consider our [5]***over-exploitation / over-emission*** of coal, oil and gas and the [6]***depletion / emission*** of these limited natural resources.

It is easy to ignore the waste we produce which is not [7]***biodegradable / bio-sustainable***, but is in fact poisonous and ends up accumulating in the air, the soil and the water.

The use of [8]***degradable / renewable*** energy, such as from wind, rain, sunlight, waves and geothermal heat, solves many of these problems.

B Complete the sentences with the verb form of the adjectives in parentheses.

1 Recent research shows that if you ____________ (*visual*) your preferred outcome in any given situation, it can improve your chances of success.

2 Top analysts have warned that the current economic crisis will ____________ (*deep*) if the government doesn't introduce a new investment program.

3 It's a good idea to ____________ (*empty*) your 'recycle bin' frequently as too many deleted files can slow down your computer.

4 Designers in China have developed robots which can absorb carbon dioxide and ____________ (*pure*) polluted city air.

5 Conducting a cost-benefit analysis will ____________ (*able*) us to decide whether the company should expand its activities into the construction sector.

6 I believe that if we ____________ (*simple*) the application process, then more people will be encouraged to take part in the volunteer program.

7 Most people agree that spending time working or studying in another country ____________ (*broad*) our understanding of other cultures.

8 Government officials hope that the international business conference will help to ____________ (*strong*) ties with their European colleagues.

GRAMMAR
Future structures

A Match each rule to an example sentence.

1 We use future progressive to describe a situation that will be in progress at a particular point in the future or to emphasize that it will cover an extended period of time. ____

2 We use future perfect to describe changes that will be completed before a particular point in the future. ____

3 We use future perfect progressive to focus on the future results of an earlier future process and/or measure the length of time of that process. ____

4 After words like *if*, *when*, *while*, etc, future tenses usually become present tenses. ____

5 Other future structures include *be on the brink of (doing)* and *be about / due / set to (do)*. ____

a Unless my new passport comes tomorrow, I won't be able to go on vacation!

b This time next week, we'll be taking our exam.

c Some astrophysicists believe they're on the verge of a very exciting discovery.

d By the time they get to Mars, they'll have been traveling for over nine months.

e They'll have finished painting the walls by tomorrow.

B Match the beginnings of the sentences (1–8) to the endings (a–h).

1 By the time I graduate, I will ____
2 The agreement is set to ____
3 By my 18th birthday, I will ____
4 I expect we'll be ____
5 The company is on the ____
6 I might have ____
7 The meeting is due ____
8 I'll be studying for my geography exam while ____

a be signed before the end of the year.
b brink of being sold to its biggest competitor.
c you're relaxing on the beach!
d have been studying for nearly five years!
e to take place in Paris on Tuesday.
f have visited at least 30 countries.
g seeing more of each other now we're living so close.
h finished my work by eight o'clock. I'll call you if I have.

PRONUNCIATION
Sounding persuasive

A Decide if each sentence is an example of exceptionalism (A), empathy (B) or flattery (C).

1 I can tell you're a good judge of character! ____
2 Maybe I can get you a special deal – just let me speak to my boss for a moment. ____
3 Well, we all have to watch what we spend these days, don't we? ____
4 You look like someone who takes very good care of himself. Do you work out? ____
5 I know *exactly* what you mean! ____
6 Wow, that's a very good question. Nobody's ever asked me that before. ____

B Read the sentences from Exercise A aloud. Try to sound as persuasive as possible. Remember that you can do this by speaking more loudly/quietly or faster/slower and using rising or falling intonation.

3.1 **C Listen to the sentences from Exercise A. Practice saying the sentences in the same way as the speakers do in the recording.**

PRONUNCIATION
Stress-shift words

A Look at the words in bold and decide if they are verbs or nouns.

1 If you **rewrite** the essay without the **extracts**, I **suspect** your score will **increase** because it has a lot of positive **attributes**.

2 Ignoring his **protests**, the judge **rejected** his appeal because his **conduct** had been so poor, but he was **transferred** to an open prison and he was **permitted** to have access to a computer.

3 We asked the singer what he **attributed** his success to, and he said that he had **progressed** in the business because he hadn't given up, even when he had been publicly **insulted** in the press.

4 I didn't like these computers at first, but now I'm a **convert** and I plan to do some **research** to find out if I can **upgrade** my own at a reasonable price.

5 The island doesn't have many **exports** and they **import** a lot of goods, so the prices are much higher after **transportation** costs have been added.

6 Reports **conflict** as to whether the **conflict** was started by ticket holders or the security guards.

B Underline the part of each bold word in Exercise A which is stressed.

3.2 **C** Listen to the sentences to check your answers in Exercise B.

GRAMMAR
Negative inversion

A Find and correct the mistakes in the sentences.

1 Not only Jake was a good businessman, but he was also a kind person.

____

2 No sooner had we arrived when it started to rain.

____

3 By no means this is over.

____

4 Under no circumstances you must disturb me.

____

5 Not once they said thank you.

____

6 No way I am ever going back there!

____

7 Only after I insisted replaced they the broken phone.

____

8 Not since I was a child I have felt so excited.

____

B Complete the extract from a story with one word in each blank. Sometimes more than one correct answer is possible.

They had told Alex when he was younger that the surveillance was for everybody's good. It was a mark of progress, to keep everybody safe – nothing to be feared. But today was the first time he had actually been followed – at least, he thought it was.

[1] ____________ in a million years did he imagine he was important enough to be followed! Yet no [2] ____________ had he stepped off the number 7 bus than he realized that the guy was there again, the same middle-aged man wearing glasses and a leather jacket. Not [3] ____________ had Alex seen him at lunchtime outside the restaurant, but he had also seen him when he arrived at work in the morning. Now, hardly had Alex reached the end of his street when he was struck by a terrible realization, 'No way [4] ____________ I want him to see where I live!' he thought.

Acting as naturally as possible, Alex crossed over and, turning right, started heading away from his house. Only [5] ____________ he had walked for another five minutes did he risk looking over his shoulder. The man had gone. Alex didn't have enough information to assume the worst, but [6] ____________ was he prepared to go home just yet. Under [7] ____________ circumstances did he want the man to find out his address. But as night started to fall, Alex realized that he didn't have a Plan B.

VOCABULARY
Verb–noun collocations

A Choose the correct options to complete the sentences.

1 In some areas the tourism industry can ***make / do*** more harm than good.
2 The business did badly last year and we've ***seen / delivered*** little progress so far this year.
3 You're just ***demonstrating / perpetuating*** the myth that all volunteers want is a free vacation.
4 If you get offered a place on that course, you should ***make / seize*** the opportunity.
5 If the manager doesn't ***set / attain*** clear objectives, how can the staff know what to do?
6 I don't think we're going to ***succeed / achieve*** our sales goals this month.
7 If you ***made / did*** a concerted effort, you might get the job finished on time.
8 When the factory opens in the village, it will ***take / bring*** benefits to the whole community.

B Complete the sentences with the verbs in the box.

brought displayed made make perpetuate seize set take

1 We've ________ great advances in technology since the turn of the century.
2 TV programs often ________ stereotypes about different social groups.
3 The figures ________ an imbalance and we began to suspect theft.
4 You know, we're always going to ________ limited progress unless we change the management structure.
5 Do you think the new factory has ________ more benefits to the area than problems?
6 I think this is a golden opportunity which we need to ________ with both hands.
7 I think you'll like him if you ________ the time to get to know him.
8 I probably failed because I hadn't ________ realistic goals for myself.

READING

A PREDICT You are going to read an article about the pros and cons of technological progress. Before you read, answer the questions.

1 What areas of life have benefitted most from technological progress?

2 What might be some long-term problems caused by technological progress?

B READ FOR GIST Read *The cost of progress*. Were any of your ideas from Exercise A mentioned?

C READ FOR COSTS AND BENEFITS Read *The cost of progress*. What are the costs and benefits in these areas of technological progress? Write notes to complete the table.

	Benefits	Costs
Communications		
Medicine		
Industry		

D REFLECT Choose one of the areas discussed in the article. Do you think the benefits of technological progress outweigh the costs? Why/Why not?

Glossary

by-product (n) an unintended result
etch (v) to delineate or impress clearly
longevity (n) the fact of living a long life

The cost of progress

From voice-activated speakers to endless options for online socializing, sharing and posting, it's clear that many of us are enjoying the benefits of technology. At the same time, we're hearing more voices that raise concerns at the rate of technological development and our lack of forward thinking about the potential costs it may bring.

To consider the balance between benefits and costs, we looked at three areas of technological and scientific progress: communications, industry and medicine.

Many people can't live without their phones, the new computers in their hands. Smartphone users continue to increase worldwide. Phones enable us to keep in touch with family, friends and colleagues with ease. But are these advantages perhaps superficial? Are they simply what people have always done but on a much larger scale? Well, not really – phone technology now does so much more, allowing us to navigate, shop, entertain ourselves, record our vacations and socialize in an endless stream of new ways. And many businesses couldn't function without this technology as rapid communication broadens their area of operations, as well as speeding their business up.

But has anything been lost along the way? Having grown up in a world before cell phones, I'm acutely aware of the random strings of numbers still etched in my memory. The landline from my friend's parents, for example. I think I can live without this information but are we losing our capacity to memorize or do simple calculations? Even if this may not seem very dramatic, what if it is a symptom of a general loss of mental skills? Could it affect the whole learning process?

In medicine, technology has improved healthcare enormously. In some countries, it's now possible to see a doctor online if required. Operations can be performed by robots, guided by doctors at a distance. Research into diseases – aided by technology – has brought new medicines to combat and even prevent them, though at some expense. There's no doubting both the short- and long-term benefits for individuals in this case. And yet, increasing longevity does raise new concerns and issues. We need to address how to finance pensions and ensure adequate care for older people. We also need to consider any negative impact that healthier older people may have on the job market. If people work longer, will it limit opportunities for younger workers?

Technology has improved efficiency in industry. A by-product of machines doing the heavy and repetitive work is that people don't have to do this. However, this means that skills which have been handed down through the generations are slowly being lost. Automation is good for the economy of the country as a whole and sometimes allows governments to spend more on social and engineering projects. The downside is that more and more jobs being done by machines may mean more and more people out of work, unless we as a society are able to quickly adapt to the harsh realities of retraining or working a shorter working week.

The scientific and technological progress we see taking place today is awe-inspiring – both wonderful and frightening. While the benefits of technology are unquestionable and life has improved for millions of people, we can't ignore the potential costs that progress brings. The need for more radical technological regulation could become greater in the future.

LISTENING

A If you were going to undertake voluntary work, which of these projects would you choose and why?

- helping to clean a beach
- working in a youth/community center
- helping to protect wild animals

3.3 **B LISTEN FOR TECHNIQUES** Listen to a conversation about a 'voluntourism' project in Tanzania and check (✓) the sentences you hear.

1 I bet you know a lot about important social and environmental issues, right? ☐
2 It's probably *the* most important event in the calendar. ☐
3 I can see you're a very smart guy. ☐
4 You're a kind-hearted person, aren't you? ☐
5 I'm *so* glad you asked. ☐
6 Just imagine the view from there. ☐
7 Can you visualize that? ☐
8 It's *absolutely* stunning! ☐
9 I really appreciate it. ☐
10 How good is that? ☐

C Which of the sentences that you checked in Exercise B make use of a persuasive technique? Is it exaggeration, a leading question or personalization?

3.3 **D LISTEN FOR SPECIFIC INFORMATION** Listen again. Decide if the statements are true (T) or false (F).

1 Steven feels disappointed because there is too much information. *T / F*
2 Joanna says she has spoken to many people visiting the Expo already. *T / F*
3 If Steven travels to Tanzania, he will help to build a school. *T / F*
4 Steven's lack of building skills is not a problem. *T / F*
5 The accommodations provided will not be luxurious. *T / F*
6 Steven would prefer to be paid for his work on the project. *T / F*
7 Steven will pay for food, accommodations, flights and administration costs. *T / F*
8 Joanna succeeds in persuading Steven to sign up for the trip. *T / F*

Glossary

bricklaying (n) building walls using bricks

E REFLECT Would it be easy for a salesperson to persuade you to buy something? Why/Why not?

WRITING

A Read the email and answer the questions.

1 Who do you think Gerry Pierce is?

______

2 Who is he writing to?

______

3 What is the purpose of his email?

______

B PERSUASIVE TECHNIQUES Read the email again and write the number of a paragraph (1–5) next to each persuasive technique (a–e). You will use one paragraph twice.

a using fact and figures ___
b appeal to readers' fears ___
c flattery ___ ___
d using technical terms ___
e linking weaknesses with strengths ___

WRITING PRACTICE

A PREPARE You are going to write a persuasive email about introducing new technology, equipment or ideas into a work environment. Think about the answers to these questions and write notes.

1 What is the work environment: business, educational, hospital, recreational, other?
2 What is your role?
3 Who are you writing to?
4 What are you persuading them to introduce?

B PLAN Organize your notes from Exercise A into a plan.

- Use an appropriate structure for a persuasive email.
- Use the techniques for persuasion from Writing Exercise B.

C WRITE Write your email in 220–260 words. Use your plan to help you.

To: Teachers' Workroom
From: Gerry Pierce
Subject: Interactive whiteboards

Dear All,

1 As you know, I have been pressing the Board of Directors to upgrade our classrooms for some time now. Thanks to your efforts, this college has an excellent academic record and reputation. Yet I notice some potential students' disappointment when they are shown around the facilities and see that we are behind the times with regard to the latest educational tools.

2 I know that some of you have doubts about the upgrades, mainly regarding costs and how it might affect your jobs. But I would also remind you that no teacher wants to be left behind either. Smart classrooms are becoming the new standard. We risk losing potential students and also making our job prospects worse if we do not keep up.

3 You'd be surprised at how much we spend on dry marker pens, erasers, chalks and blackboard painting each year. Interactive whiteboards need none of these things. Equipped with the latest LCD touchscreen displays with striking visuals and graphics, these boards have everything in one place to enhance learning. If we can get the go-ahead, there will be training sessions for us all. Most students these days are tech-savvy, so you can always ask them for help if you get stuck!

4 Although acquiring interactive whiteboards will require some initial investment, we will benefit in the long run by saving on teaching materials and attracting more students (see attached costs/benefits analysis). The new equipment would bring more ease and flexibility to the learning experience and will make it more interesting and fun for both students and teachers.

5 I am pleased to work with some of the smartest and best trained teachers at Broadwick College. You deserve better. So let's get together on this and equip the college with smart classrooms. With your support, I'm sure the Board will be persuaded to provide the funds to bring us into the 21st century, so I ask each one of you to reply to this email stating your commitment to my proposals.

Best regards,

Gerry

PRONUNCIATION
Adding information

A Read the pairs of sentences (a and b) aloud. Try to step down to a lower pitch when you read the underlined information in sentence b.

1 a A lot of people say that eating superfoods can make you more intelligent.
  b A lot of people say that eating superfoods – which include fish, broccoli, nuts and spinach – can make you more intelligent.

2 a Generally speaking, exercise can help you stay more alert.
  b Generally speaking, exercise – even something gentle like walking or stretching – can help you stay more alert.

3 a Starting work early in the morning is meant to make you more productive.
  b Starting work early in the morning, as opposed to working late into the evening, is meant to make you more productive.

4 a Some people are great believers in 'mindfulness'.
  b Some people are great believers in mindfulness, the practice of living in the moment without thinking about the past or worrying about the future.

4.1 **B** Listen to the sentences from Exercise A. Practice saying the sentences in the same way as the speakers do in the recording.

VOCABULARY
Conceptual metaphors

A Match the sentences (1–7) to the related conceptual metaphors (a–e). You will need to use some of the letters more than once.

1 Tim had always been eager to get ahead, but now his career had reached a dead end. ____
2 Unlike her sister, who obviously had a brilliant mind, Stella came across as less bright. ____
3 I've invested countless hours in this business – I won't let it fail. ____
4 My suggestions for the new project were shot down in flames. ____
5 Don't make her angry – she has a really fiery temper. ____
6 Carl lost his cool and threw the folder across the room. ____
7 I could tell as he listened to my speech that he was getting ready to attack. ____

a time = money
b anger = heat
c argument = war
d life = journey
e light = intelligence

B Complete the story with the words in the box.

attack backwards cool crossroads defenseless shed tempered wasted

Sarah felt she had reached a [1] ____________ in her life. Everything depended on her winning this business negotiation. She knew if she wasn't successful it would be a huge step [2] ____________ for her. At the very least, she would have [3] ____________ the last year.

The key thing would be to get her client Ricardo on her side. He was very hot-[4] ____________ at the best of times, and people often felt [5] ____________ when he really went on the attack. A conversation with her colleague Patricia [6] ____________ a lot of light on how she should approach Ricardo.

Although she was nervous on the day of the negotiation, she successfully kept her [7] ____________. She was so calm and diplomatic that Ricardo didn't even realize she was implementing a careful plan of [8] ____________.

The negotiation was a success. Of course both sides won. But Sarah won a little more than Ricardo this time.

GRAMMAR

Conditionals without *if*

A **Choose the correct options (a, b or c) to complete the sentences.**

1. ______ you had $1 million – what would you do first?
   a Were
   b Imagine
   c Should
2. Ask a random sample of people if they are intelligent ______ most of them will say they are.
   a so that
   b and
   c therefore
3. ______ me you needed money, I would have helped gladly.
   a Had you told
   b Were you telling
   c Should you tell
4. Are you coming to the party – ______ it's still on?
   a assuming
   b were
   c believing
5. ______ a little research and you will find that augmented reality will have a huge impact on learning and many other areas in the future.
   a Had you done
   b Should you do
   c Do
6. ______ harder, you might just pass the test next time.
   a Were you to try
   b Had you tried
   c Should you have tried
7. ______ he come back tomorrow, we'll try to help him.
   a Imagine
   b Should
   c Providing
8. ______ we to consider your offer, when could you start?
   a Were
   b Suppose
   c Should

B **Complete the second sentence so that it has a similar meaning to the first sentence. Write three words including the word given. Do not use the word *if* in the second sentence.**

1. If you have any queries, you can refer to the briefing document.
   TO
   You could refer to the briefing document ______ have any queries.
2. If you see Kevin, tell him to call me.
   SHOULD
   ______ Kevin, tell him to call me.
3. If I'd taken a few more practice tests, I might have passed the exam.
   DONE
   I might have passed the exam ______ a few more practice tests.
4. Would you have an implant if someone gave you the chance?
   SUPPOSE
   ______ given the chance, would you have an implant?
5. If they knew it was dangerous, they wouldn't have gone there.
   REALIZED
   ______ the danger, they wouldn't have gone there.
6. If you ask anyone, they will tell you where to go.
   ASK
   ______ they will tell you where to go.

VOCABULARY
Science and research; Thinking

A Complete the sentences with the correct form of the words in the box.

conclude conduct demonstrate experiment finding hypothesize norm participant speculate

1 We never ________________ any really interesting ________________ in our science lessons, and I think that's why I was never attracted to science as a career.

2 This study clearly ________________ that it's time for a rethink about social ________________ in this country – I think we've been getting it all wrong.

3 We really can't ________________ about what's going to happen – we have no idea!

4 Now that we have gathered the data from both younger and older ________________ in the study, what can we ________________?

5 Scientists often ________________ that things exist long before they can be proven.

6 After we did the research, we arranged a meeting to discuss our ________________ with the development team.

B Choose the correct options to complete the text.

Are you a PROBLEM-SOLVER?

To some people, problem-solving comes naturally. They can [1]***overthink / troubleshoot*** a problem by following a logical train of thought, just like a doctor diagnoses an illness. Or in some cases they are instinctively good at understanding how things work, so if they apply themselves to a problem, they will have a [2]***eureka / common*** moment sooner or later and get to the bottom of the problem.

To be a practical problem-solver, you need to have a certain amount of [3]***wishful / common*** sense. Some people who are great at solving problems are a little [4]***eureka / eccentric*** – they behave in strange ways sometimes. Others might be good problem-solvers, but they are really [5]***curious / absent***-minded in their daily lives, always forgetting where they left things or failing to finish their sentences when they speak.

So how do you improve your problem-solving skills? Well, it helps if you are [6]***curious / eccentric*** about the world – if you're the kind of person who likes to take things apart to see how they work. Also it pays not to [7]***troubleshoot / overthink*** a problem – you sometimes need to step away from it and the answer will come to you naturally.

But to a few people, being able to solve complicated problems is just [8]***absent / wishful*** thinking – they are never going to be able to do it and if they try, they might end up doing more harm than good!

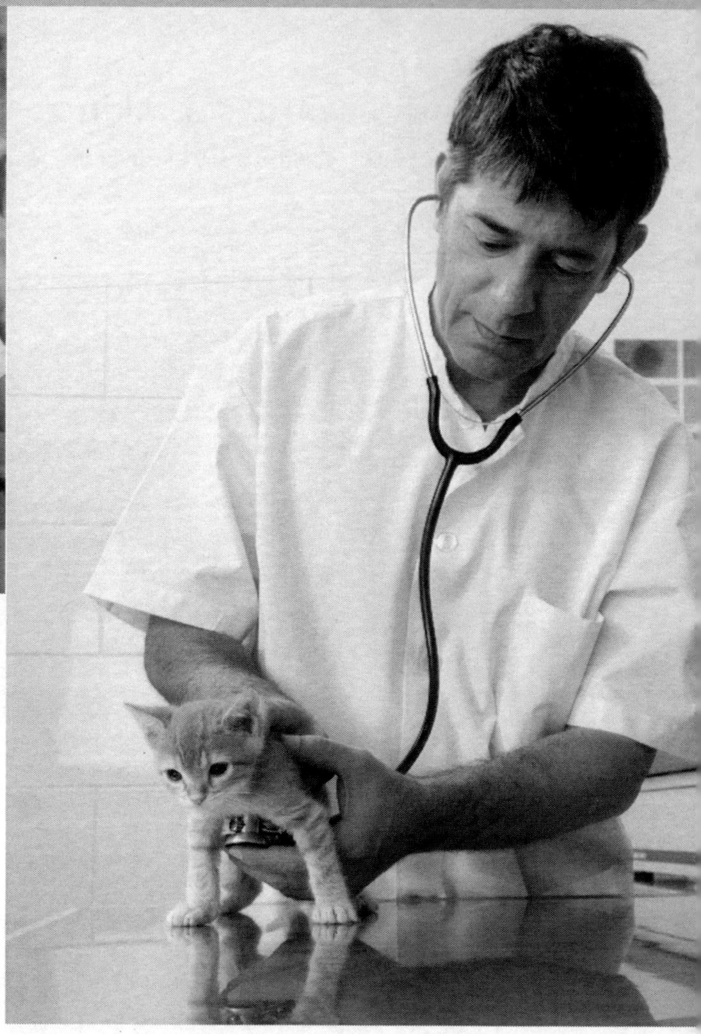

GRAMMAR
Wishes and regrets

A Match the sentences (1–8) to the meanings (a–h).

1. I would love to have been a participant in that study. ___
2. They should have told participants what to expect. ___
3. I wish I could be a participant in that study. ___
4. We should have used more participants. ___
5. If only there were more studies like this. ___
6. I would love to be a participant. ___
7. They should not to have told us what they were doing. ___
8. I wish I wasn't a participant. ___

a. I am not a participant.
b. There weren't enough participants.
c. They explained too much.
d. They didn't explain.
e. There aren't enough studies.
f. I can't be a participant.
g. I am a participant.
h. I wasn't a participant.

B Complete the sentences with one word in each blank.

1. Tim wishes he ___ been able to study science in college.
2. If only we ___ go anywhere in the world.
3. Claire would love to ___ visited that college.
4. If ___ I knew what job I wanted to do.
5. My brother ___ he was a student again – he would do things differently.
6. Sam ___ have gotten a better certification.
7. If only I ___ more confident.
8. They ___ have studied when they had the chance.

PRONUNCIATION
Adding information or changing the topic

A Look at the underlined words and phrases. Are they used to add information (A) or change the topic (B)?

1. Reading is a good way to keep your mind active. On top of that, books can be a good conversation starter. ___
2. Plus, he also lied about his qualifications. Anyway, we won't get stuck on that – let's move on. ___
3. I'm going to be out of the office from Wednesday onwards. In other words, if you need me, you'll have to catch me on Monday or Tuesday. ___
4. You can, of course, mention this in your essays. By the way, I'm expecting essays next week from all of you. ___
5. I find I process information better if I hear it rather than see it written down. In the same way, I would rather listen to books than read them. ___
6. After that, he was living in Berlin … So, as I was saying, his work is very important for our studies. ___

B Read the sentences in Exercise A aloud, paying attention to the intonation on the underlined sections.

4.2 **C Listen to the sentences from Exercise A. Practice saying the sentences in the same way as the speakers do in the recording.**

READING

A PREDICT What is intelligence? How would you define intelligence?

B READ FOR GIST Read *What is intelligence?* and *An intelligence test*. Were any of your ideas from Exercise A mentioned?

C READ TO IDENTIFY Match the stylistic features (1–6) to the texts (A or B). Underline in the texts examples of each feature.

1 formal vocabulary ____
2 contractions ____
3 an impersonal style ____
4 complex sentences ____
5 idiomatic language ____
6 short sentences ____

Glossary

contest (v) to disagree
have green fingers (v phr) to be good at growing plants and flowers
sublime (adj) extremely good

D REFLECT Think about the answers to these questions.

1 Have you changed your opinion about what intelligence is? Why/Why not?
2 Do you agree with the conclusions in the articles? Why/Why not?
3 Is there anything in the articles that you want to research further?

A What is intelligence?

Intelligence is one of the most debated subjects in psychology. While there are many competing theories, there is no generally accepted definition. Some believe that it is a single, overall ability, while others believe it comprises a variety of skills, aptitudes and talents. However, despite theoretical differences most agree that how people adapt to their environment is key to understanding intelligence.

Adaptations can occur in numerous situations. It involves making a change in oneself to manage new situations or environments effectively. In certain circumstances, it may mean manipulating the environment itself to suit one's purposes: for example, re-routing a river to irrigate farmland.

Developmental psychologist Howard Gardner in his book *Frames of Mind: The Theory of Multiple Intelligences* (1983) was the first to propose the concept of multiple intelligences. He argued that theories which considered intelligence to be a single, general ability often focused on logical-mathematical intelligence, whereas, the human brain had much wider cognitive abilities.

While many theories of intelligence still accept the notion that intelligence has more than one dimension, the popularity of Gardner's theory among some educators brought criticism on the grounds that its claims cannot be scientifically validated and the criteria Gardner selected are arbitrary (White, 2005).

B An intelligence test

I've seen the smartest people do the stupidest things. I once watched, fascinated, as a philosophy major removed a faucet without first turning off the water supply. OK, his degree wasn't in plumbing, but a tiny bit of common sense would have stopped him.

This got me interested in the idea of different types of ability. So I decided to think about where my strengths lie. What are the things that I'm smartest at?

Personally I love being out in nature and cats and dogs seem to like me. But I have to admit, I don't have green fingers. My one attempt to grow an avocado tree failed miserably. OK, maybe I should be looking elsewhere.

Sports? I certainly have developed a little soccer knowledge over the years, but I'm more comfortable on the couch telling you about it than on the soccer field!

Am I a lost cause? Many psychologists now think that how we adapt to new situations is important in measuring how intelligence works. I think what I've realized is that intelligence, at least for me, is less about having a special talent or ability and more about having the right attitude.

LISTENING

A You are going to listen to a discussion about human versus animal intelligence. Which of these abilities do you associate with humans (H), animals (A) or both (B)?

- communicating a complex message ______
- learning from experience ______
- understanding abstract concepts ______
- being able to count ______
- using tools to achieve an objective ______

4.3 B **LISTEN FOR GIST** Listen to a discussion about human versus animal intelligence. Did the speakers mention any of the topics from Exercise A?

4.3 C **LISTEN FOR MAIN IDEA** Listen again and circle the name of the speaker who mentions these ideas.

1. humans' ability to cope with abstract ideas *Nadia / Charles*
2. the biases of scientists *Nadia / Charles*
3. writing systems *Nadia / Charles*
4. sea creatures communicating with each other *Nadia / Charles*
5. humans lacking certain skills *Nadia / Charles*
6. learning through imitation *Nadia / Charles*

4.4 D **RECOGNIZE LOGICAL FALLACIES** Listen to some extracts from the discussion. Are they examples of generalization (A) or anecdotal evidence (B)?

1 ______

2 ______

3 ______

Glossary

accumulation (n) the process by which something (e.g. knowledge) is collected over time

echolocation (n) the biological process used by some animals to navigate

skewed (adj) not accurate because it is affected by somebody's personal opinion

E **REFLECT** Think about the answers to these questions.

1. Which speaker do you agree with more? Why?
2. Which animal do you think is the most intelligent? Why?
3. Which animal is most helpful to humans? Why?
4. What makes us different to animals?
5. What makes us similar to animals?

WRITING

A How important do you think a healthy diet and exercise are for brain function?

B Read the report. Number the paragraphs in the order they should appear and give them the correct paragraph headings from the box below.

Conclusion Discussion Introduction Methods Results

Investigating the effects of diet and exercise on cognitive function

a ________

The group participating in the exercise program performed much better on thinking tests than they had previously. This was seen mainly in executive function: planning, problem-solving and decision-making. The group on the dietary program showed no improvement in executive function. The group on the exercise and diet program showed the greatest improvement in cognitive function, including the speed at which they processed information. All these findings are in line with the original study.

b ________

We strongly believe that in those with age-related cognitive decline, a change in lifestyle involving aerobic exercise and a healthy diet may improve cognitive function. But it can be concluded that more research is needed to confirm this claim.

c ________

Forty adults with an average age of 65 were divided randomly into four groups: 1 Those put on an aerobic exercise program. 2 Those given dietary advice and put on a healthy diet. 3 Those put on a course of both exercise and dietary advice. 4 A control group who didn't alter their dietary or exercise habits at all. Each group stayed on their course for six months.

d ________

This report replicates a study on the effect of diet and exercise on older adults (Behrer, Erikson and Ambrose, 2013). The study suggests that the participants may improve their thinking skills by regular aerobic exercise and good nutrition. This experiment supports the original findings.

e ________

The original researchers found that while there was no proven therapy to halt or reverse age-related cognitive decline, lifestyle changes might delay decline by several years. But the researchers stressed that a larger and more long-term study was needed to confirm their results. Unfortunately the scale of this experiment (much smaller than the original) means it cannot add much to the existing evidence. However, the experiment did produce similar results to the original.

C Read the report again. Find and underline examples of hedging.

Hedging

In a scientific report unless something is a well-established fact, we can use hedging to make our claims less strong and less open to criticism.

1 auxiliary verbs such as *may*, *might* and *could*
2 adverbs such as *probably*, *possibly* and *likely*
3 verbs that allow for some doubt, such as *seem*, *appear*, *suggest*, *indicate*
4 introductory phrases to qualify, such as *We believe*, *We understand*, *In our view*

WRITING PRACTICE

A **PREPARE** Read about a similar experiment. Imagine you have recently replicated it. Underline anything you think should be included in a report.

In a similar study, 1000 people aged between 60 and 70 were divided into two groups. The study aimed to discover the effect of a program of diet, exercise and brain training on cognitive function. All participants were given the same tests at the beginning of the study and at regular intervals throughout the period. The first group, called the control group, received nothing more than advice. The second group, called the intervention group because the experiment intervened in their behavior, were put on an intensive program of diet, exercise and brain training. At the end of the experiment, the intervention group scored 25% higher than the control group on cognitive function and 83% higher on executive function.

B **PLAN** You are going to write a report about the experiment. Write notes to help you.

- Use the facts you underlined in Exercise A. You can also use your imagination to come up with information not mentioned in the text.
- Organize your ideas into an appropriate structure for a report, using the paragraph headings from Exercise B.
- Use hedging words/phrases where appropriate.

C **WRITE** Write your report about the experiment in Exercise A in 220–260 words.

D **EDIT** Edit your report. Check:

- spelling and punctuation
- the register is formal
- an appropriate structure has been used.

GRAMMAR
The passive voice

A Choose the correct options to complete the sentences.

1. If you make a noise in here, you'll ***have* / *get*** thrown out.
2. Do you remember ***to be* / *being*** introduced to your manager for the first time?
3. At school, we were made ***go* / *to go*** running – even in the snow!
4. The printer was cheap, but the ink needs ***to be* / *being*** changed very frequently.
5. Do you think it's time for me to ***be* / *get*** my hair cut?
6. Is it possible that we're ***been* / *being*** watched through our smartphone cameras?
7. If I'm successful, I'll be ***congratulated* / *congratulating*** by everyone.
8. The office ***had* / *got*** broken into over the weekend.

B Complete the profile with the correct passive form of the verbs in parentheses. Sometimes more than one answer is possible.

Greg Fitzjohn: board game designer

So how did I get my dream job? That's what I [1] ________________ (*always / ask*). Well, the truth is, it happened almost by accident. I [2] ________________ (*invite*) by a college friend who designed board games to spend a few hours in the office with him, just to see what he did. I didn't want to get in the way, so Friday afternoon [3] ________________ (*choose*) – as it's usually a quiet time. It was getting close to five o'clock when my friend's boss burst into the office. I sat quietly listening. The atmosphere was tense. From what I understood, a new game [4] ________________ (*develop*) and a final check needed [5] ________________ (*do*) by Monday. Someone was [6] ________________ (*going to / make*) work over the weekend, but nobody had been found. So I volunteered. The boss dismissed the idea at first, saying things like, 'No, we couldn't. You're not an employee. What if something [7] ________________ (*break*) or lost?' But then she agreed. I took the game home, delivered my report on Monday morning, and on Monday afternoon, I was offered a job!

PRONUNCIATION
Expressing disbelief

A Read the conversations. Underline the words and phrases the second speaker uses to express disbelief.

1 **A:** Well, what does it say on your contract?
B: Contract? What contract?

2 **A:** So, we'd want you to take the game home and, well, just play it as much as possible.
B: Really? Is that all I have to do?

3 **A:** I think they're looking for people to stay late tonight.
B: No way! Again? I'm leaving at the usual time. Not a minute later.

4 **A:** I heard Jones got fired for stealing from his employer.
B: Seriously? After all he's done for the company!

5 **A:** If you hate your job so much, you should leave.
B: Are you joking? Where will I get another job? How will I live?

6 **A:** They say we'll get a bonus if this goes well.
B: Yeah, right! I'm sure *that's* going to happen!

5.1 **B Listen to the conversations. Check your answers to Exercise A.**

C Practice saying the sentences in the same way as the speakers do in the recording in Exercise B.

VOCABULARY
Competition and cooperation

A Match the beginnings of the sentences (1–8) to the endings (a–h).

1 We thought our team would lose but their determination ____
2 To finish the project before the deadline, three of us ____
3 The man who has been accused of the crime is said to be ____
4 The country depends on the support of its ____
5 The complicated rescue operation was ____
6 You win points each time you force your ____
7 Everyone is part of a community, so we think even of our ____
8 In the end, our experience allowed us to ____

a allies in matters of national security.
b collaborated and got the job done quickly.
c opponent into making a mistake.
d cooperating with the police.
e overcome the other team.
f coordinated by the heads of the emergency services.
g prevailed in the end.
h rival players as friends.

B Complete the sentences with the prefix *out* and the correct form of the verbs in the box.

do number play run smart weigh

1 The police ____________ him – he fell right into their trap.
2 Josh was very competitive and particularly hated being ____________ by younger soccer players.
3 Look – I know it's not ideal, but the advantages ____________ the disadvantages, so we have no choice.
4 Helen's younger and in better shape than me – I'd never ____________ her in a race.
5 Not wanting to be ____________ by his neighbor, Clive bought exactly the same car.
6 In my English class, female students ____________ males by two to one.

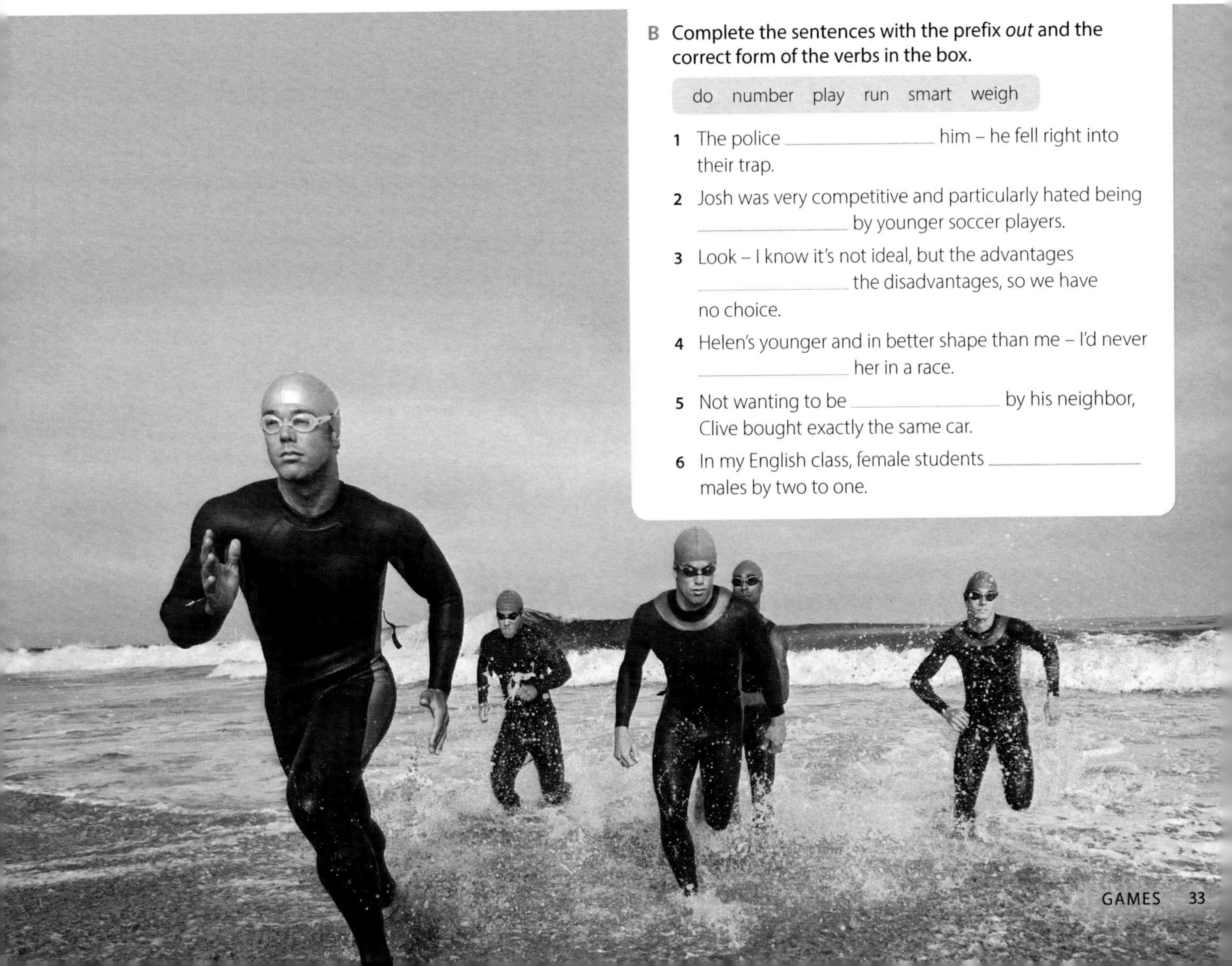

PRONUNCIATION
-*ate* words

A Read the sentences aloud. Pay attention to the way you pronounce the underlined words.

1 I don't know if it's appropriate to take flowers or not – these cultural differences are complicated.

2 I find that TV show fascinating – I want to see who gets eliminated next.

3 The estimate for the work was 500 dollars, but that company is not usually very accurate with its initial numbers.

4 If you cooperate fully with the authorities, they can eliminate you as a suspect.

B Listen to the sentences from Exercise A and check the pronunciation. 5.2

VOCABULARY
Reporting verbs; Motivation and manipulation

A Choose the correct options to complete the sentences.

1 They ***alleged / urged*** that he had stolen the money but they had no real evidence.

2 You have to ***acknowledge / imply*** that you were wrong.

3 Daniel ***instructed / asserted*** that he was going to lead the team.

4 Fiona ***boasted / implied*** that she was ready to leave the company although she didn't use those words exactly.

5 I ***doubt / speculate*** that anyone can do a better job than Jeanette – she's so good.

6 After losing every match, the manager was forced to ***clarify / conclude*** that his team wasn't very good.

B Complete the text with the words in the box.

act coax inclined nuts spur steer tap

John Murphy
December 5, 2019 at 10:20 am

My company was suffering from a lack of motivation among the staff. We've always tried to [1] ________ into their natural enthusiasm for the job, but there were problems getting teams in different parts of the office to talk and collaborate. Six months ago, we introduced a games room at work and this has really helped. The staff went [2] ________ for Ping-Pong, foosball and board games. We found we no longer had to [3] ________ managers from different teams into attending meetings and company social events. Playing games really [4] ________ them on to cooperate as they became naturally curious about each other's work. Reply

Eloise Waters
December 5, 2019 at 10:48 am

You've highlighted one of the biggest arguments for more opportunities to socialize at work. Staff members are [5] ________ to become demotivated when they don't feel they have shared goals or they feel they are working against other teams. This can make people suspicious and territorial. Then they [6] ________ against the interests of the company and ultimately their own interests. My best advice is to increase opportunities to socialize and play together which gently [7] ________ people toward understanding and trusting their colleagues. Reply

GRAMMAR
Passive reporting structures

A Choose the correct options (a or b) to complete the sentences.

1 He's our longest-serving employee – it can be assumed ___ the truth.
 a to tell
 b that he is telling

2 ___ have employed the services of a professional coach.
 a People rumor that the team
 b The team is rumored to

3 They're easily the best, so ___ to win.
 a they are expected
 b is expected for them

4 The company is said ___ a major investment in the area.
 a to be planning
 b to plan

5 It is widely considered ___ motivation and salary go hand in hand.
 a for
 b that

6 Yes, he is alleged ___ the money, but that hasn't yet been proved.
 a to have stolen
 b he has stolen

7 The robbers ___ armed and extremely dangerous.
 a are known that they are
 b are known to be

8 ___ to be interested in selling off part of the company.
 a It is understood
 b They are understood

B Complete the passive reporting structures with the correct form of the reporting verbs in parentheses.

1 It has ___ (*report*) the fire broke out in the main building around midnight.

2 It ___ (*know*) that there are at least two other people involved.

3 Billy ___ (*understand*) traveling to Spain right now.

4 The escaped prisoner ___ (*believe*) heading for Brazil.

5 Parachuting from cliffs ___ (*rumor*) popular in the park.

C Rewrite the sentences so that they start with the words in bold.

1 It's understood that **the exam** has been postponed.

___

2 Everyone knows that **computer simulations** are extremely useful.

___

3 It's thought that **our math professor** is writing a book about Game Theory.

___

4 We expect that **everybody** will vote for the favorite.

___

5 It was alleged that **the other player** had cheated.

___

D Think of ways of completing the following sentences.

- It's expected that …
- It's rumored that …
- It isn't widely known that …
- It's sometimes said that …
- It's believed that …

WHY WE PLAY GAMES

We are often told that it's the taking part that matters, but if we're being honest, it's winning that really counts. Speaking of which, in a backgammon competition, I once beat the national champion. [1]___ Well, when I say beat, I mean beat him once in a best-of-five-games match! But for a very short while, I felt like a champion. We're also told sports – particularly team sports – teach us valuable life skills, such as cooperation and fair play. Admirable qualities no doubt, but winning makes you feel a lot better about yourself.

So – just uncomplicated fun and the pleasure of winning? Maybe not. Psychologists claim that it goes much deeper than that. [2]___ According to Deci and Ryan's self-determination theory, games satisfy a number of important subconscious needs which may not be met in real life. The three main ones are competency, which is our need to feel in control of situations or at least be able to deal with them successfully. Related to this is our desire for autonomy or independence – the feeling that the choices we make are our own. And third, there's what's called relatedness, which is our social instinct – the need to feel important to others in some way and that we are contributing to something larger than ourselves. Work usually fulfills this need in the everyday world.

If that sounds like too much psychology for a simple game of conkers, let's look at some other reasons for our attraction to games. And as we've mentioned conkers, let's use it as an example. For those who don't know, it is a game played by children in the UK where each child has a large nut tied on the end of a piece of string. Most of the fun in playing conkers is in finding ways to strengthen your horse-chestnut

READING

A PREDICT Look at the pictures and think about your answers to these questions.

1 Have you played any of these games?
2 Why do you think people play these games?
3 Why do people play games in general?

B READ FOR GIST Read *Why we play games*. What different games does the author mention?

C UNDERSTAND ASIDES Read the article again and fill in the blanks (1–6) with the asides (a–f).

a I know I do.
b You're impressed, I can tell!
c Well, they would, wouldn't they?
d Go on, admit it!
e Beat that if you can!
f Cheating in other words!

D READ FOR DETAIL Read again. Answer the questions.

1 Why do you think the writer tells us the anecdote about the backgammon game?
2 What benefits of team sports are mentioned?
3 What three principal human motives are satisfied by game playing?
4 What factor does the writer think is common to all games?
5 How do games help you get in a state of 'flow'?

Glossary

make-believe (n) the activity of pretending that something is real
pay-off (n) positive result
trance (n) state where you are awake, but not conscious of your surroundings

E REFLECT Think about the answers to these questions.

1 Do you think playing video games is a way to escape from reality?
2 In what ways can games prepare people for real-life situations?

so that it is hard enough to smash your opponent's, but is unbreakable itself, by soaking it in vinegar, for example, or baking it. [3] ___ The process sometimes takes days. I can't think of a game that doesn't involve competitiveness. Don't pretend you don't get pleasure from outsmarting an opponent. [4] ___

But what, apart from competitiveness, holds our interest? Modern video games offer clear examples of what attracts us to games and keeps us playing, but I think the same features apply, though less obviously, to old-fashioned board games. Many people still enjoy games like Clue – [5] ___. These features include a story-telling or make-believe element – often a reflection of the real world – but with more freedom of choice and without real-world consequences. They allow you to act out roles you never would in real life. You have goals and your efforts are rewarded and allow you to measure your progress. Entertainment and escapism with a pay-off. [6] ___

Total absorption in games is another aspect of our fascination with them. You reach a state that athletes call being 'in the zone' and psychologists call 'flow'. You are so totally focused and in control that nothing can distract you, and you slip out of time.

LISTENING

A Work in pairs. Look at the picture of the video gamer. What might be some problems with this activity?

5.3 **B LISTEN FOR MAIN IDEA** Listen to the podcast. Check (✓) only the things that are true according to Andrea.

1. If somebody becomes less social, it can be a warning that there is a problem. ☐
2. Games are the main reason people get addicted to the internet. ☐
3. Governments have solved the problem by passing laws restricting screen time. ☐
4. The problem isn't limited to younger users. ☐
5. Many gamers feel more at home in an artificial community. ☐
6. Gaming encourages people to do more physical activity. ☐

5.3 **C LISTEN FOR SOLUTIONS** Listen again and choose the correct options (a, b or c) to complete the sentences.

1. According to Andrea, gamers
   - **a** need to be banned from playing games by law.
   - **b** should be supported to set boundaries themselves.
   - **c** should be stopped from playing by their parents.
2. Andrea thinks the deeper cause of the problem is
   - **a** our desire for rewards and community.
   - **b** social networks refusing to be positive role models for gamers.
   - **c** the gamer's determination to play games.
3. The problem can be solved
   - **a** by recognizing the causes and supporting the gamer.
   - **b** by encouraging them to adopt a different persona.
   - **c** by governments and parents working together to make gamers do more physical activity.

Glossary

persona (n) particular personality or character – often different to the one you normally have

D REFLECT Which solution do you believe would be most effective in tackling problems with video gaming?

WRITING

A Read the report and answer the questions.

1 Which company is the report for?
2 What is the purpose of the report?
3 Which company had some dissatisfied staff?

B USING DEPERSONALIZATION Rewrite the sentences/ clauses (a–e) in formal, depersonalized language. Then use them to fill in the blanks (1–5) in the report. More than one answer is sometimes possible.

a They observed higher levels of motivation in both staff and customers,
Higher levels ____________,
b An app on the staff's smartphones records all the activities they perform and turns them into points.
All activities ____________.
c … we decided we should conduct an investigation …
… it ____________ …
d I should mention, however, that an app such as the one *GetFit* uses …
It ____________
e They have also introduced incentives for those doing work such as cleaning.
Incentives ____________.

WRITING PRACTICE

A PREPARE Read the task below and write notes.
You have been asked by the manager of the sports equipment company you work for to write a report about using games to attract customers to your company's exhibit space at a trade fair. Think about how traditional games (bingo, spin the wheel, etc), apps and virtual reality may help draw customers to your exhibit space.

B PLAN You are going to write a report for the task in Exercise A.

- Organize your notes into an appropriate structure for a report.
- Use formal, depersonalized language.
- Give your recommendations in the final paragraph.

C WRITE Write your report in 200–300 words. Use your plan to help you.

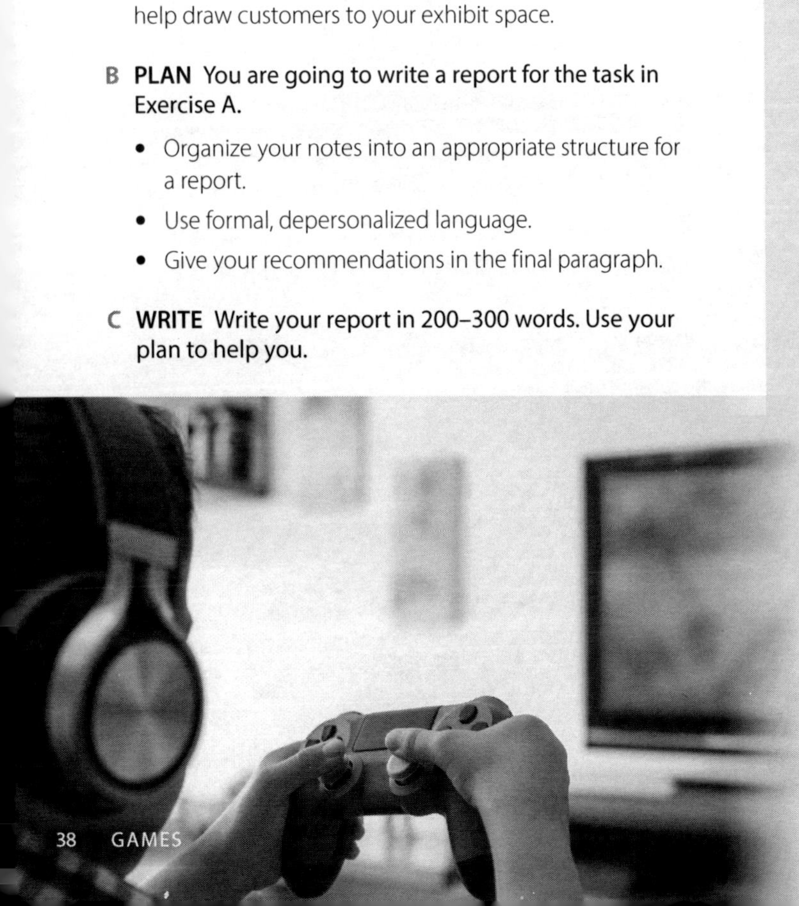

Using games to improve motivation and efficiency at *Sports Unlimited*

Background

At a recent meeting of the Board of Directors of *Sports Unlimited*, [1] ____________ into similar businesses where gamification has been introduced to improve staff motivation and efficiency. This report summarizes the research and offers some recommendations to the Board.

Case study 1: GetFit

This company's use of gamification is well known. [2] ____________ When a certain level is reached, the user is rewarded, either with a bonus or a company perk, such as a day off. The app has been made available to customers as well and has proved to be highly popular. [3] ____________ but more so in the latter. However, some staff were worried about losing their privacy.

Case study 2: World Sports Inc.

Here gamification has been introduced not only to increase motivation but as a training tool. Staff are encouraged to adopt different roles within the company via an app that sets them tasks appropriate to that position. This provides a deeper knowledge of all aspects of the business and encourages staff to think about their future in the company. Since its introduction, there has been a 25% increase in efficiency. [4] ____________ As with *GetFit*, it is a points/rewards system and has increased motivation for people engaged in these tasks.

Recommendations

For our purposes here at *Sports Unlimited*, I would recommend an app similar to that used by *World Sports Inc.*, or one very like it, as the most suitable for in-house use, which would not be too expensive to install. [5] ____________ but for customer use only, would help increase brand awareness. Finally, it should be noted that some form of a points/rewards game is always a good motivator.

Irregular Verbs

Base form	Simple past	Past participle
be	was/were	been
become	became	become
begin	began	begun
break	broke	broken
bring	brought	brought
build	built	built
buy	bought	bought
can	could	been able to
catch	caught	caught
choose	chose	chosen
come	came	come
cost	cost	cost
cut	cut	cut
drink	drank	drunk
eat	ate	eaten
fall	fell	fallen
feel	felt	felt
find	found	found
forget	forgot	forgotten
get	got	got
give	gave	given
go	went	gone/been
grow	grew	grown
have	had	had
hear	heard	heard
hit	hit	hit
hold	held	held
hurt	hurt	hurt
keep	kept	kept
know	knew	known
leave	left	left
lend	lent	lent
let	let	let
lose	lost	lost
make	made	made
mean	meant	meant
meet	met	met
must	had to	had to
pay	paid	paid
put	put	put
read	read	read
ride	rode	ridden
run	ran	run
say	said	said
see	saw	seen
sell	sold	sold
send	sent	sent
set	set	set
shut	shut	shut
sing	sang	sung
sit	sat	sat
sleep	slept	slept
speak	spoke	spoken
spell	spelled	spelled
spend	spent	spent
stand	stood	stood
steal	stole	stolen
take	took	taken
teach	taught	taught
tell	told	told
think	thought	thought
throw	threw	thrown
understand	understood	understood
wear	wore	worn
win	won	won
write	wrote	written

PHONETIC SYMBOLS											
Single vowels			Diphthongs			Consonants					
/ɪ/	fish	/fɪʃ/	/uw/	news	/nuw/	/p/	pen	/pen/	/s/	snake	/sneɪk/
/iː/	bean	/biːn/	/eɪ/	face	/feɪs/	/b/	bag	/bæg/	/z/	zoo	/zuː/
/ʊ/	foot	/fʊt/	/ɔɪ/	boy	/bɔɪ/	/t/	tea	/tiː/	/ʃ/	shop	/ʃɒp/
/uː/	shoe	/ʃuː/	/oʊ/	nose	/noʊz/	/d/	dog	/dɒg/	/ʒ/	television	/'telɪvɪʒən/
/e/	egg	/eg/	/ju/	use	/juz/	/ʧ/	chip	/ʧɪp/	/m/	map	/mæp/
/ə/	mother	/'mʌðər/	/aɪ/	eye	/aɪ/	/ʤ/	jazz	/ʤæz/	/n/	name	/neɪm/
/ɜː/	word	/wɜːrd/	/aʊ/	mouth	/maʊθ/	/k/	cake	/keɪk/	/ŋ/	ring	/rɪŋ/
/ɔː/	talk	/tɔːk/				/g/	girl	/gɜːrl/	/h/	house	/haʊs/
/æ/	back	/bæk/				/f/	film	/fɪlm/	/l/	leg	/leg/
/ʌ/	bus	/bʌs/				/v/	verb	/vɜːrb/	/r/	road	/roʊd/
/ɑː/	arm	/ɑːrm/				/θ/	thing	/θɪŋ/	/w/	want	/wɒnt/
/ɒ/	top	/tɒp/				/ð/	these	/ðiːz/	/j/	yes	/jes/

Audio scripts

UNIT 1

Lesson 1.4, Listening, Exercise B
1.4 **W = Woman M = Man**

W: Have you watched this year's GenZ Round-up?

M: No, what's that?

W: It's a video series that the video site GenZ creates at the end of every year. It has – like – well, everything that's happened in the last 12 months.

M: OK. It sounds interesting. Like – a round-up of the year?

W: Exactly. They did the first one in 2012, and that kind of set a trend. They've been doing one every year since. Each year has a slightly different title though, for example, 2016 was 'GenZ Round-up: The Best of 2016' and 2017 was 'GenZ Round-up: Here's 2017'.

M: And this year's?

W: Well, here's the thing. This year's was really bad. Everybody hated it and it got really bad reviews!

M: Why?

W: A lot of viewers said that it didn't include enough content creators – you know – the people who actually make the site what it is. Also, it included a lot of celebrity endorsements and people thought that was a bit cheesy.

M: Hey! I've had a great idea! Why don't we make our own 'Round-up' video?

W: Actually, a lot of people are doing just that – making their own videos.

M: OK. Let's do it! You're really media-savvy. What should we include?

W: As a general rule, we should include all the latest trends, the most popular videos – the ones that went viral, for instance, and everyone watched.

M: Like when that TV announcer fell off his chair live on air a few years ago?

W: Exactly!

M: What else?

W: It's a good idea to include top news stories from the previous year, too. I mean, the really big ones that everybody talked about. You don't need to include a lot of detail – maybe just an image of a person who was in the headlines with some bright colors or special effects.

M: Do you know how to do that?

W: Yes, don't worry. It's not difficult. I have a program on my computer that does it. The trick is to keep the video moving at a really fast pace and to use a variety of different media. For example, we could add in some animation – clips from superhero movies or popular cartoons.

M: This is going to be great! What about those little – what do you call them – you know – those photos with the funny text that everyone shares and passes around?

W: Memes?

M: Yes, that's it.

W: You're right. We definitely have to include last year's most popular memes. I know – let's ask our friends to tell us their favorites, and those are the ones we'll include.

M: Good idea.

W: There's one thing this video really needs and that's influencers.

M: What do you mean?

W: Influencers – they don't watch videos or 'like' the content, they *are* the content, they *set* the trends. I'm talking about GenZ personalities and vloggers – like Daisy Trekker, for instance.

M: What is a vlogger exactly?

W: Oh, come on! You must know what a vlogger is.

M: Well, kind of …

W: Basically, they record video diaries of different things – sports, playing computer games, testing new products or just their ordinary lives.

M: So, they're like … trendsetters?

W: Exactly. It's worth including their videos because everybody loves them and then maybe people will watch *our* video. Generally speaking, we have to include stuff that's *relevant*. It has to be new – or newish anyway. And we can't forget to include some clips from fashion and beauty vlogs – those are really popular, too. My favorite is Bonella – she has more than 11 million subscribers.

M: That's amazing! So, what are we waiting for? Let's get started.

W: OK. I'll go and get my laptop …

UNIT 2

Lesson 2.4, Listening, Exercise C
2.3 **P = Presenter R = Ruth**

P: Architecture may not be the first discipline which springs to mind when somebody mentions 'art', but some of the most famous artists in the world – like Michelangelo and Raphael – were architects as well as painters. In the modern world, architects like Frank Lloyd Wright and Le Corbusier command world-wide respect and admiration.

Today, we're going to be looking at the work of Frank Gehry, a Canadian-American architect whose designs include the Walt Disney Concert Hall in the US and the Guggenheim Museum in Bilbao, Spain. Here to tell us about him is art historian Ruth Butler. Good morning, Ruth, thanks for joining us.

R: Good morning. Thanks for inviting me.

P: Frank Gehry has become so famous that he's almost a household name. He's been referred to by some commentators as a 'starchitect'. Tell us a little bit more about the man.

R: Of course, Nick. A starchitect is a reference to his kind of – well, his 'star' status in the world of architecture, but actually, he doesn't like that term at all. He's proud of his work and highly respected, but he doesn't like the idea of celebrity status. So … Gehry was born in Canada. His family was of Polish origin and his name was originally Frank *Goldberg* – he changed his name to Gehry while he was studying at the Southern California School of Architecture.

P: Tell us about his early career. Was he immediately successful?

R: No, not really. Like most great artists, he went through difficult times before he made it big. After finishing his studies – he also studied city planning at Harvard University – he worked for a number of different firms and tried his hand at furniture design, as well as renovating his own home in a way which would become – well, the style that he's now known for.

P: His signature style, you could say?

R: Yes, that's right.

P: Tell us a little bit about that.

R: Well, his early work was a reaction against the modernist buildings of the 60s and 70s which were springing up all over the cities of America. There was a lot of glass, a lot of sharp angles and forms which reflected advances in science, and industry and technology of the period. Gehry wanted to emphasize the human angle, and of course contextual integrity was very important to him.

P: I think you'll have to explain that to our listeners, Ruth.

R: Yes, of course. The 'context' of a building is its location, the other buildings and structures around it, the immediate environment I would say. It was important to Gehry that his work – his buildings – reflected their surroundings, the historical or social aspects of where they were – the context if you will. So … um … back to his style … His style is very 'sculptural' you know. He uses materials and forms shapes and structures almost in the way a sculptor might. He's probably best known for his use of unusual materials and for the creation of bold and unconventional shapes through the use of those materials.

P: We have some photos of Gehry's work here in the studio.

R: Yes, this one is an excellent example of what I'm talking about. This building is known as the Dancing House and it's in Prague in the Czech Republic. The building looks almost as if it's moving from side to side like two dancers. This is very different from the traditional lines and forms of previous buildings.

P: Awesome!

R: During the 80s and 90s, he was offered commissions throughout the world: Prague – as we've seen – Spain, the US, Germany. And his reputation just grew and grew from then on really. Arguably his most iconic building is the Guggenheim Museum in Spain which you mentioned at the beginning of the program, Nick. Visitors to this, and other buildings of Gehry, have commented that the space he's created inside is more impressive than the objects it was designed to house.

P: It does look like – well – like a sculpture in its own right.

R: Exactly. It's really an architectural landmark – literally and metaphorically.

P: Thank you, Ruth, for this insight into the life and work of one of the world's greatest living architects.

R: I just hope it inspires some of your listeners to read and learn more about him, Nick. I think they'll find his work fascinating.

UNIT 3

Lesson 3.4, Listening, Exercise B
3.3 **J = Joanna S = Steven R = Rachel**

J: Hi, Steven! Welcome to the World Aid Expo. I'm Joanna.

S: Hello. Um … how do you know my name?

J: Your name badge?

S: Oh, yes of course. Silly me! Um, hi Joanna.

J: So, Steven. I bet you know a lot about important social and environmental issues, right? You look like a well-educated person. Are you a student?

S: Yes, I am actually. I must say I didn't expect this much from the Expo, but I was so wrong. It's fascinating – all the different stalls, a lot of information, new ideas …

J: Absolutely. It's probably *the* most important event on the calendar, definitely the most interesting! Hey, listen … I just get a feeling about you. You're a kind-hearted person, aren't you? I bet you're someone who actually helps other people. You genuinely care about their problems, their situations. Am I right?

S: Well, yes, I …

J: To be honest, there are so many visitors this year, but I haven't approached them because I don't feel that I've seen anyone … who's, well, who's *genuine*. Somebody who feels as passionately about helping others as I do – as our organization does.

S: What does your organization do exactly?

J: I'm *so* glad you asked. We work with local communities in Tanzania – a beautiful country … really, you're going to *love* it when you go there … We work with schools, women's groups, youth and community groups. This year, we're building a library in the town of Arusha. You can see Mount Kilimanjaro from there. Can you visualize that?

S: Yes, it sounds amazing.

J: It's *absolutely* stunning! And *you* can be part of our vision, Steven. We really need volunteers to come out to Tanzania and help with building the library.

S: Um … don't you need special skills – you know – to … um … build a, well, a building? I'm afraid I don't know much about bricklaying or concrete or electrics or anything.

J: That's not a problem! Not a problem at all. I just know that your passion and your commitment are what we need on this project.

S: Well, I don't know. What would it involve exactly?

J: You fly out to Tanzania – we organize one-week and two-week trips. You'll be staying in local accommodations – nothing fancy, but I'm sure you won't mind that. You'll meet our local coordinator who'll allocate a workplace to you. Maybe we'll even organize trips to local sights. Sounds a little too good to be true, doesn't it?

S: Um … it sounds interesting.

J: Of course, this *is* a volunteer project, so obviously you won't be paid.

S: Oh, of course not. I wouldn't expect that.

J: What do you say? Are you interested?

S: Yes, I'm definitely …

J: That's fantastic! I bet you're good at creative writing, aren't you? When you come home again, we'd love you to write about your experience.

S: Well, I *am* quite …

J: Amazing, I'll put you down for the writing! Excellent. Of course, there are some expenses. We don't want local people having to contribute to the cost of volunteers' food. So, we ask for a donation from you of $500 for that – that's per week.

S: Yes, of course.

J: And then there are the flights – just $980. We arrange everything, don't worry. And we have some really good news this year – no administration costs, the organization is covering that side of things. So, nothing to pay there. How good is that?

S: Do you have an application form?

J: Yes, absolutely. If you'd like to go over there and speak to the woman in the green jacket – she's our team leader. She'll give you a form to fill out and you can discuss payment with her.

S: Thanks so much Joanna. I'll see you in a little while. I'll come back when I've completed the application.

J: Hi, Rachel! Welcome to the World Aid Expo. I'm Joanna.

R: Oh hi. Wow … how do you know my name?

UNIT 4

Lesson 4.4, Listening, Exercise B
4.3 **L = Leah N = Nadia C = Charles**

L: In today's *Looking further*, we're asking, 'Just how smart are human beings?' To help me answer this, I have two guests in the studio: Charles Bragg from the London Animal Rights Center and Professor Nadia Abbas. Good morning to you both.

N: Hello.

C: Hi.

L: Nadia – what's your view? Are human beings really the most intelligent creatures on the planet?

N: As a lecturer in anthropology, I would have to answer 'yes'. For many years, scientists and academics have carried out experiments which conclude that we are indeed the most intelligent species on the planet. We can understand abstract concepts and use an accumulation of knowledge to manipulate our environment, and of course our use of language is second to none. But perhaps most important of all is our ability to reason – to have the kind of discussion which we're having right now!

C: But what you're saying has been 'proved' historically is actually just an *assumption* by scientists. Just because we've always believed something doesn't necessarily make it true. I genuinely don't think scientists can be trusted on this issue because they, quite simply, never question their own opinions and assumptions.

N: Well, I agree with you on that point Charles – of course our views and beliefs change over time – but, nevertheless, the vast body of research proves that humans are the most intelligent species.

C: But Nadia – experiments are a reflection of the people carrying them out. Much of the research you're talking about was skewed by those scientists' existing views of human intelligence and was designed to support those views. When people have tried to analyze animal intelligence, they've always focused on a strictly human definition of intelligence. I mean – so what if a squirrel can't count to ten? Squirrels don't need to be able to count to ten!

N: I agree in part with what you're saying, Charles. Some of the qualities which we regard as essentially human – reasoning, language and so on – are just one *form* of intelligence. In fact, in some ways, it's perhaps meaningless to judge animal intelligence by human standards. But …

C: Well, there you are! It's a question of different degrees of intelligence. I mean – think about dogs. I was taking my dog out for a walk last week and I was amazed that while most of the people were listening to headphones or not talking at all, he was picking up on the smells that other dogs had left. If that's not evidence that dogs have equally complex forms of communication, I don't know what is. My dog is very good at communicating his demands to me and getting me to do what he wants.

N: Well, of course, but that's a matter of conditioning. There's no comparison though between the way in which a dog communicates basic needs and the incredibly complex systems of verbal and written communication which humans have developed over thousands of years.

C: Well, let me give you another example. We know that killer whales have a rich and complex language. In fact, I was watching a TV documentary about it just last night. Dolphins have individual names based on whistle signals. That's proof that animals can communicate just as well as humans do.

N: OK, I think you're confused about what I'm saying. But let's leave language aside for the moment. The way in which we are able to accumulate knowledge and use that knowledge to manipulate our environment is key. This ability has even allowed us to send a spacecraft to Mars.

C: But that's precisely my point! Animals don't want or need to go to Mars! But they *also* have incredibly complex systems which they use on an everyday basis – I mean … humans have traveled to the moon, but have they perfected a system of echolocation such as bats use? No!

N: I do agree that some research is leading us to question our assumptions about animal intelligence, but this *still* doesn't allow us to conclude that animals are equally intelligent. Let me give you an example. If we compare chimps and humans, when it comes to tasks which require 'social learning', like watching somebody else completing a task and then copying their behavior, human toddlers are way ahead of chimpanzees.

C: Yes, but …

L: Charles, Nadia – I think this debate could probably go on for hours, but that's all we have time for today, so we're going to have to leave it there.

UNIT 5

Lesson 5.4, Listening, Exercise B
5.3 **J = John A = Andrea**

J: Today, we're talking to psychologist Andrea Preston about the consequences of too much time spent gaming and online. And we're also asking what can be done about it. So, Andrea, should we be worried?

A: Hi John. Well, as worried as we are about other forms of compulsive behavior, yes. Spending too much time playing video games is a serious issue for many people. Of course, there's a difference between someone who enjoys video games and even the more avid gamer who spends most of their free time on gaming. What we're talking about here is when gaming gets in the way of everyday life.

J: Right! With two children at home, I think I might know what you mean. But at what point does it become a problem?

A: Well, signs to watch out for are preferring to spend time alone in front of a screen instead of spending time with family and friends. In some cases, gaming can interfere with everyday tasks like washing, eating and sleeping. I guess when you have some countries introducing laws to regulate the amount of time young people can spend playing online video games, you know you should be paying attention.

J: I guess so. But that does seem like a step too far. Should governments be calling the shots?

A: Hmm … for some it does seem like an obvious solution. Governments could pass laws preventing players from participating in online games for more than a certain period of time. Problem solved. But the amount of time spent playing games may in fact be a symptom of deeper psychological issues. We should actually attempt to help gamers create personal boundaries and balance around gaming rather than banning or restricting by law. But more importantly, we should treat the underlying causes of a person's reliance on such games.

J: Surely all this comes down to parenting, don't you think?

A: Well, it depends. Conventional wisdom might say that parents aren't being hard enough on this issue, you know, by setting clear boundaries with their children. But there are two things we need to be clear on. First, the problem doesn't just affect younger gamers. We're talking about adults as well. Second, while yes of course friends and family can play a positive role, being stricter and making rules won't necessarily get to the root of the problem.

J: So, what is at the root?

A: There are two things that I think usually get missed in the discussion. First of all, we need to be clear that games tap into very human desires. We crave challenges and games are set so they are never too easy or difficult. Games also tap into our desire for rewards.

J: I have to admit that's what keeps me playing my children's games. Usually when they're not around!

A: You're not alone John. But there's more. It would be a mistake to ignore the social aspect of online games – after all, for many, gaming is also a form of social media. Many gamers feel a strong sense of belonging in their online communities, despite the fact that they will probably never meet in real life.

J: So, you're saying we need to recognize that games fulfill specific needs that we all have.

A: Yes, well put! Parents and friends of gamers should understand that. It's not about telling someone they can't do something. They should encourage gamers to replace the positive feelings they get through gaming with things like physical exercise. And if it's a serious problem, they should encourage the gamer to see a doctor or health professional.

J: So, it seems we can have too much of a good thing after all! Andrea, thanks so much for joining us.

A: Thanks for having me John.

Answer key

1.1 Dress for success

VOCABULARY

A

1 follow **2** casual **3** outfit **4** set **5** sportswear
6 uniform **7** stands **8** gear **9** oversized **10** baggy

B

1. wind you up
2. snapped up
3. catches your eye
4. throwing money down the drain
5. make a seamless transition
6. in the long run
7. off-the-rack
8. tailor-made
9. are on a tight budget
10. for peanuts

GRAMMAR

A

1 c **2** b **3** a **4** f **5** e **6** d

B

1. it
2. how
3. that
4. not
5. was
6. why
7. where
8. What

C

1. the problem of
2. The fact that
3. How she spends her money
4. do not/don't mind wearing

1.2 Trendsetting

GRAMMAR

A

1. as quickly as
2. dramatically
3. latest
4. louder
5. a higher
6. Easily the most
7. a considerably higher
8. great
9. deeper

B

1 c **2** d **3** b **4** f **5** a **6** e **7** h **8** g

VOCABULARY

A

1. hyper-influential
2. tech-savvy
3. waterproof
4. amateurish
5. disaster-prone
6. undelete
7. user-friendly
8. super-lucky

B

1. heat-resistant
2. largish
3. spammy
4. rethink
5. cheesy
6. unmuted
7. idiot-proof
8. ultra-/super-/hyper-cautious

PRONUNCIATION

A

1. He's suggesting one solution, but there <u>are</u> others.
   He's suggesting <u>one</u> solution, is that the best he can do?
2. They told me to work on <u>this</u> project, so that's what I'm doing.
   They said the same to me, and that's what <u>I</u> am doing.
3. He suggested that <u>the</u> biggest problem is overseas sales.
   But you don't realize that the biggest problem <u>is</u> overseas sales.
4. I <u>can</u> do it; the question is whether I want to do it.
   I can do it, too, but I don't know <u>when</u>.
5. Do <u>you</u> think this will be a problem?
   Without question, this <u>will</u> be a problem.

C

1. I was determined not to say <u>anything</u> that could get me in trouble.
2. Contrary to what you said, I <u>do</u> enjoy gardening.
3. Bill got the contract <u>and</u> a promotion, so he's happy.

1.3 Reading

READING

B

1 e **2** c **3** a **4** b **5** d

C

1. increasing
2. friendly
3. rare
4. unlikely
5. exciting, unusual
6. open, outgoing

D

1 d **2** f **3** a **4** c **5** e **6** b

1.4 Listening

LISTENING

B

2, 3, 6, 7, 9

C

1 round-up
2 reviews
3 (TV) presenter
4 special effects
5 animation
6 friends
7 vlogger
8 new/newish/relevant

1.5 Write a blog post

WRITING

A

Possible answers

1 format, repetition of keywords/phrases, etc
2 layout, pictures, font style, etc
3 publish relevant content, use keywords, update your content regularly, etc

B

1 c 2 d 3 a 4 b

C

1 successful, blog, post, blog post
2 By structuring it well and using headings, the search engine will pick up on key topics and help improve your ranking. Also, being reader-friendly, it will attract more readers, and more readers means more clicks. This also helps to improve ranking.
3 Add links and more posts to your website.
4 'For more tips ...', 'click on the icon below'.

WRITING PRACTICE

C

Model answer

4 FAQs about electric vehicles

If you are concerned about the environment and want motoring to be cheaper and safer, then electric vehicles (EVs) are the thing for you. As the trend for EVs grows, more and more people are getting interested. Here are answers to four of the most frequently asked questions (FAQs).

1 Are they really eco-friendly?

Yes, absolutely. They don't burn fuel, so there are no emissions. By not using gas or diesel, they are not adding to the gases that cause air pollution and contribute to global warming. Driving an EV substantially reduces your carbon footprint.

2 Are they economical?

Again, yes. Because you're not paying for gas to keep your EV running, you save a lot on fuel. Charging your EV could cost less than $1, depending on the type of vehicle. EVs are also cheaper to maintain. EV engines have far fewer parts that can go wrong than conventional cars, and they are easier to fix.

3 Are they safe?

EVs are no less safe than other cars. We're not talking about driverless cars – you're still in charge. However, if you do have an accident, you are safer in an EV as there is little chance of it catching fire.

4 What about performance?

EVs are often more roomy than conventional cars because they have smaller engines. They also provide a smoother drive than conventional cars. As the market has become bigger, EV performance levels have improved greatly. One charge can take you between 100 and 200 miles, and as more people buy EVs, there will be more charging stations all over the country.

EVs are growing in popularity and are here to stay. They are clean, safe and cheap to run. What's not to like?

For more information about electric vehicles, click on the link below.

2.1 The story behind it

VOCABULARY

A

1 g 2 b 3 c 4 h 5 d 6 a 7 e 8 f

B

1 groundbreaking
2 overrated
3 pretentious
4 hilarious
5 unconventional
6 thought-provoking
7 sensational
8 tedious

C

1 sensational
2 iconic
3 repetitive
4 appalling
5 underrated
6 acclaimed

GRAMMAR

A

1 was being prepared
2 called
3 was waiting
4 had been damaged
5 had had
6 were told
7 wasn't I informed
8 had been snowing

B

So – big day today. Important meeting with some clients so I had to get to the office early. I got up at five, had a quick cup of coffee and **left** the house at 5:20. I got half way to the office when I realized that I **had forgotten** my phone. Can you believe it? I **had driven / had been driving** for at least half an hour already, so I really didn't feel like going back, but I **had** no choice. So, that delayed me by about an hour. And when I finally got to the office, I **was given** a message that my boss wanted to see me urgently. I ran to her office. I could see through the glass door she **was talking** to my clients, who **had** already arrived. Oh no! Luckily, she wasn't annoyed and my clients were fine. The meeting went well, and by lunchtime, we **had** agreed on everything.

2.2 Creative people

VOCABULARY

A

1 wall **2** canvas **3** start **4** draw **5** fresh **6** bounce **7** run **8** state **9** trust **10** immerse

B

1 late **2** part **3** thick **4** self **5** highly **6** world **7** open **8** well

GRAMMAR

A

1 d **2** e **3** f **4** b **5** a **6** c

B

1 a **2** c **3** a **4** b **5** a **6** b **7** c **8** b

2.3 Reading

READING

A

Possible answers

These words are connected to the topic and appear in the text: engineer, bridge, proposal, railway, carriage, survey, overground, construction

C

1 (Great) Britain/The UK and France
2 Eurobridge
3 six years (from 1988 to 1994)

D

1 b **2** b **3** a

2.4 Listening

LISTENING

A

Positive: awesome; groundbreaking; iconic; sensational; thought-provoking
Negative: appalling; pretentious
Neither positive nor negative: unconventional

B

Possible answers

1 architect
2 extremely
3 modern/unconventional

D

1 world-wide respect
2 celebrity status
3 difficult times
4 surroundings / (immediate) environment / context
5 unusual materials
6 more impressive

2.5 Write a review

WRITING

B

a 5 **b** 1 **c** 3 **d** 2 **e** 4

C

1 c; Organized in such a way as to surprise and delight the visitor, the paintings are presented in an unusual fashion.
2 b; Monet, born in 1840, continued painting until the mid-1920s.
3 a; French Impressionist painter Monet painted Rouen Cathedral several times.

WRITING PRACTICE

C

Model answer

The Hayward Gallery, located in the Southbank Center in Central London, is world-famous for its exhibits of contemporary art. The current exhibit focuses on the work of David Shrigley. Best known as a cartoonist, Shrigley demonstrates his talents as a fine artist here.

There are 240 works on display in this exhibit: cartoons, of course, but also photographs, some of which could be called absurdist, sculptures and … other things. Well, what would you call a cookie nailed to a wall? Also, paintings, animations and an installation of a swarm of insects made out of black metal wire.

All this would seem to indicate that Shrigley has roots in surrealism, and some pieces bring Salvador Dali and Rene Magritte to mind. The insects in the installation seem to refer to the ants that recur in Dali's paintings and Magritte's bright green apple makes an appearance. He also likes to play with the relative size of things, with small things made large beyond any possible usefulness, such as a cup of tea.

This is not to say that he is just a follower or imitator. He has his own style, with a wacky sense of humor, absurd, surreal and sometimes dark. There are those who don't consider this serious art – whatever that is – but jokes can often get you closer to the truth than seriousness. If not closer.

Well worth a visit, this exhibit is mischievous and full of fun, and I bet you will find it hard not to laugh out loud in the hushed atmosphere of the art gallery.

3.1 Progressive design

VOCABULARY

A

1 emissions
2 carbon-neutral
3 offset
4 sustainable
5 over-exploitation
6 depletion
7 biodegradable
8 renewable

B

1 visualize
2 deepen
3 empty
4 purify
5 enable
6 simplify
7 broadens
8 strengthen

GRAMMAR

A

1 b 2 e 3 d 4 a 5 c

B

1 d 2 a 3 f 4 g 5 b 6 h 7 e 8 c

PRONUNCIATION

A

1 C 2 A 3 B 4 C 5 B 6 C

3.2 Better … or worse?

PRONUNCIATION

A and B

1 If you **rewrite** (verb) the essay without the **extracts** (noun), I **suspect** (verb) your score will **increase** (verb) because it has a lot of positive **attributes** (noun).
2 Ignoring his **protests** (noun), the judge **rejected** (verb) his appeal because his **conduct** (noun) had been so poor, but he was **transferred** (verb) to an open prison and he was **permitted** (verb) to have access to a computer.
3 We asked the singer what he **attributed** (verb) his success to, and he said that he had **progressed** (verb) in the business because he hadn't given up, even when he had been publicly **insulted** (verb) in the press.
4 I didn't like these computers at first, but now I'm a **convert** (noun) and I plan to do some **research** (noun) to find out if I can **upgrade** (verb) my own at a reasonable price.
5 The island doesn't have many **exports** (noun) and they **import** (verb) a lot of goods, so the prices are much higher after **transportation** (noun) costs have been added.
6 Reports **conflict** (verb) as to whether the **conflict** (noun) was started by ticket holders or the security guards.

GRAMMAR

A

1 Not only **was** Jake ~~was~~ a good businessman, but he was also a kind person.
2 No sooner had we arrived **than** ~~when~~ it started to rain.
3 By no means **is** this ~~is~~ over.
4 Under no circumstances **must** you ~~must~~ disturb me.
5 Not once **did** they **say** ~~said~~ thank you.
6 No way **am** I ~~am~~ ever going back there!
7 Only after I insisted **did/would they replace** ~~replaced they~~ the broken phone.
8 Not since I was a child **have** I ~~have~~ felt so excited.

B

1 Never/Not
2 sooner
3 only
4 do/would
5 after/when
6 neither/nor
7 no

VOCABULARY

A

1 do
2 seen
3 perpetuating
4 seize
5 set
6 achieve
7 made
8 bring

B

1 made
2 perpetuate
3 displayed
4 make
5 brought
6 seize
7 take
8 set

3.3 Reading

READING

C

Communications

Benefits: everyday ease of keeping in touch, long-term effects on business

Costs: loss of mental skills (e.g. memorization), loss of practical skills (such as mental arithmetic), may interfere with the whole learning process

Medicine

Benefits: seeing a doctor online, remote operations, improved healthcare, more effective drugs, longevity, early retirement (as an advantage)

Costs: the cost of research and the price of new medicines, the cumulative effects of increased longevity (money for pensions, care for older people) and the effect on the job market

Industry
Benefits: people no longer have to do boring jobs, efficiency, economic growth and the benefits it brings (e.g. social and engineering projects)
Costs: traditional skills are being lost, loss of jobs

3.4 Listening

LISTENING

B
1, 2, 4, 5, 7, 8, 10

C
1 leading question
2 exaggeration
4 leading question
5 exaggeration
7 personalization
8 exaggeration
10 leading question

D
1 F (He didn't expect as much but has been impressed.)
2 F (She says she hasn't spoken to many people this year.)
3 F (He will help to build a library.)
4 T
5 T
6 F (He says he doesn't expect to be paid.)
7 F (He won't have to pay administration costs.)
8 T

3.5 Write a persuasive email

WRITING

A
1 (probably) the college principal
2 the teaching staff
3 to persuade them to support his proposal of introducing interactive whiteboards to the classrooms / to ask them to reply stating their support

B
a 4 **b** 2 **c** 1; 5 **d** 3 **e** 4

WRITING PRACTICE

C
Model answer
Dear All,
I know how hard you have all worked to make a success of this start-up business. We have acquired an impressive client base for such a small and new business and it looks as if we're going to keep growing. However, looking ahead, I can see we might have some problems in the future with inadequate internet connectivity.

We all have an equal interest in the company and what I am about to propose may mean a cut in salary for all of us in the short term, but if we get fiber optic cables installed now, we will be winners in the long run. Rapid connectivity is essential in our business and fiber optic cables, as you know, provide a higher bandwidth than what we have now and can transmit data over longer distances.

What is important is that the upgrade will improve our efficiency and allow us to expand our business. Although it is expensive to install, because we are centrally located and other businesses nearby already have fiber optics, it will be easier and cheaper for us. I have attached a breakdown of the costs so you can see how much we have to reduce costs in other areas and for how long.

It would be a shame to see all your talent and skill frustrated by out-of-date technology. We have laid solid foundations and have a loyal client base, and I believe we are strong enough to face this issue. We're in this together.

You are all bright, hard-working and adventurous people, otherwise you wouldn't be here. So let's take the next step to making our business grow even stronger in the future.

Best regards,
Sam

4.1 Brain training

VOCABULARY

A
1 d **2** e **3** a **4** c **5** b **6** b **7** c

B
1 crossroads **2** backwards **3** wasted **4** tempered
5 defenseless **6** shed **7** cool **8** attack

GRAMMAR

A
1 b **2** b **3** a **4** a **5** c **6** a **7** b **8** a

B
1 were you to
2 Should you see
3 had I done
4 Suppose you were
5 Had they realized
6 Ask anyone and

4.2 Thinking and thought

VOCABULARY

A
1 conducted; experiments
2 demonstrates; norms
3 speculate
4 participants; conclude
5 hypothesize
6 findings

B
1 troubleshoot
2 eureka
3 common
4 eccentric
5 absent
6 curious
7 overthink
8 wishful

GRAMMAR

A

1 h **2** d **3** f **4** b **5** e **6** a **7** c **8** g

B

1 had
2 could
3 have
4 only
5 wishes
6 should
7 was/were
8 should

PRONUNCIATION

A

1 A **2** B **3** A **4** B **5** A **6** B

4.3 Reading

READING

C

1 A **2** B **3** A **4** A **5** B **6** B

4.4 Listening

LISTENING

B

Yes, all of them were mentioned.

C

1 Nadia **2** Charles **3** Nadia **4** Charles **5** Charles
6 Nadia

D

1 B **2** A **3** A

4.5 Write a report

WRITING

B

a 3 Results
b 5 Conclusion
c 2 Methods
d 1 Introduction
e 4 Discussion

C

Introduction: 'The study suggests that …'
Discussion: 'the study suggests that'; 'lifestyle changes might delay decline by several years'
Conclusion: 'we strongly believe that in …'; '… a change in lifestyle involving aerobic exercise and a healthy diet may improve cognitive function'

WRITING PRACTICE

C

Model answer

Introduction

This report describes a study that investigated whether a combined program of healthy eating, exercise and brain training could have an effect on cognitive function in older people. Experts agree that what is good for the heart, such as regular exercise and a healthy diet, is good for the brain.

Methods

One thousand participants aged between 60 and 70 took part in this two-year-long study. All participants were tested for cognitive function, weight and blood pressure at the start of the study and again at 6, 12 and 24 months. Participants were then randomly split into two groups. The control groups received regular advice only. The intervention group received an intensive program which comprised of diet, exercise and cognitive training.

Results

The study found that overall the scores in tests measuring cognitive function in the intervention group were 25% higher than the scores in the control group. In tests for executive function – the brain's ability to plan, organize, solve problems and make decisions – the intervention group scored 83% higher than the control group. It should be pointed out, however, that as with previous studies, the intervention group showed no improvement in memory.

Discussion

The researchers believe that the fact that 12% of the participants dropped out of the trial does not affect the results. They say their findings indicate that intervention is effective in treating the problems associated with aging and brain function. This research replicates the findings of the original study.

Conclusion

It can be concluded that a combined program of diet, planned exercise as well as 'brain training' is effective in improving age-related cognitive function.

5.1 21st century games

GRAMMAR

A

1 get
2 being
3 to go
4 to be
5 get
6 being
7 congratulated
8 got

B

1 am/'m always (being/getting) asked
2 had/'d been invited / was/got invited
3 had been chosen / was/got chosen
4 was being developed / had been developed
5 to be done
6 going to be made to
7 is/gets/was/got broken

PRONUNCIATION

A

1 Contract? What contract?
2 Really?
3 No way! Again?
4 Seriously?
5 Are you joking?
6 Yeah, right!

VOCABULARY

A

1 g
2 b
3 d
4 a
5 f
6 c
7 h
8 e

B

1 outsmarted
2 outplayed
3 outweigh
4 outrun
5 outdone
6 outnumber

5.2 Serious gaming

VOCABULARY

A

1 alleged
2 acknowledge
3 asserted
4 implied
5 doubt
6 conclude

B

1 tap
2 nuts
3 coax
4 spur
5 inclined
6 act
7 steer

GRAMMAR

A

1 b 2 b 3 a 4 a 5 b 6 a 7 b 8 b

B

1 been reported (that)
2 is known
3 is understood to be
4 is believed to be
5 is rumored to be

C

1 The exam is understood to have been postponed.
2 Computer simulations are known to be extremely useful.
3 Our math professor is thought to be writing a book about Game Theory.
4 Everybody is expected to vote for the favorite.
5 The other player was alleged to have cheated.

5.3 Reading

READING

B

backgammon; conkers; video games; Clue

C

1 b 2 c 3 f 4 d 5 a 6 e

D

Possible answers

1 to illustrate the idea of how good it feels to win
2 teaching life skills such as cooperation and fair play
3 competency: the desire to feel in control/successfully deal with situations; desire for independence/making our own choices; relatedness: feeling important to others
4 competitiveness
5 'total absorption' – you are so focused you can't be distracted

5.4 Listening

LISTENING

B

1, 4, 5

C

1 b
2 a
3 a

5.5 Write a formal report

WRITING

A

Possible answers

1 Sports Unlimited
2 to investigate how games can improve motivation/efficiency in the workplace and recommend an app
3 GetFit

B

Possible answers

a Higher levels of motivation were observed in both staff and customers, … / Higher levels of motivation in both staff and customers were observed, …
b All activities (that are) performed by staff are recorded on an app on their smartphones and (then) turned into points.
c … it was decided that an investigation should be conducted …
d It should be mentioned, however, that an app such as the one used by *GetFit*, …
e Incentives for those doing work such as cleaning have also been introduced. / Incentives have also been introduced for those doing work such as cleaning.

1 c
2 b
3 a
4 e
5 d

WRITING PRACTICE

C

Model answer

Using games to attract customers to company exhibit space at the trade fair

Background

At a meeting of managerial staff to discuss the forthcoming trade fair in Venezuela, it was decided to investigate the effectiveness of using games in attracting more potential clients to the company's exhibit space. This report summarizes the research and offers some recommendations.

Traditional games

While they are still used by many companies at trade fairs to attract customers, traditional games are not regarded as being as interesting or exciting as digital games or virtual reality. However, they should not be rejected altogether. For example, a large container filled with tennis balls was used by one company as a guessing game, with a prize for the person who guessed the correct number of balls. People are still drawn to contests such as this.

Reality and virtual reality

Games and contests in which potential clients are invited to use our own sports equipment are another possibility (see recommendations). There might be some difficulty with regard to space, which is limited and expensive. Most people are attracted to virtual reality games, especially sports, and this would be a good way of promoting our products.

Recommendations

As golfing equipment is the company's best-selling range, it is recommended that efforts be concentrated on that. It would be easy to set up an indoor putting green and hold a contest with participants using the company's equipment. It is also recommended that a driving range simulator be installed – many business people are eager golfers. This might prove to be expensive but will undoubtedly attract additional visitors to the exhibit space. As far as traditional games are concerned, the idea of the container filled with tennis balls could be transformed into a large glass jar filled with own-brand golf balls, with an attractive prize for the winner. Customer numbers would significantly increase by putting these recommendations into practice.

Notes

Notes